To
J.
John Anderson

JOHNANDERSONBOOK.COM

AN INHERITANCE INCORRUPTIBLE

A faith-inspired novel of historical
fiction based on a family legacy

By

John Doyle Anderson

Copyright © 2022 John Doyle Anderson

All rights reserved.

No content of this book may be copied, excerpted,
replicated, or shared without the permission of the
author.

Published by SuburbanBuzz.com, LLC

ISBN: 978-1-7360820-6-5

ADVANCE PRAISE

What people are saying about John's new book...

Take a trip back in time, in a front-row seat, to witness the faithfulness of God. In our crazed, fear-stricken world, John Anderson provides an escape to focus on what is certain; faith & God's faithfulness. An Inheritance Incorruptible allowed me the privilege of recounting similar 'testimonies' in my own journey. It's a must-read!

Tim R. Barker, D.Min., Superintendent/Pastor South Texas Assemblies of God Ministries

John Anderson is my friend and neighbor. We worship in the same church and to the same God who watched over me in World War 2, along with those whom you'll read about here. He is a good storyteller and is good at putting it on paper. History and faith jump off each page, and it's clear to see why the title is 'An Inheritance Incorruptible'. I have often traveled the East Texas Piney Woods area which he writes about and my wife's family lived there. Selma Newton's lifelong strong faith was reinforced by the powerful works of God that she witnessed here, just as did so many within this story. Take my advice, read on and be encouraged!

Cecil J.V. Newton, late of the U.S. Army, 87th Infantry Combat Division, active in the second advance on the Rhineland and Central Europe, 1945

When I first met Johnny, I met a man on a mission. He has a heart for people and for ministry. The writing in his book comes from a heart after God, like David in the Bible, who chased after what the Holy Spirit wanted of his life. I gladly endorse this book knowing the man and his life.

Gary Sapp, Lead Pastor, Harvest Church, West Monroe, LA

DEDICATION

This book is dedicated first and foremost to my Lord Jesus Christ. His story is the life within the heart of *An Inheritance Incorruptible*. My enjoyment of the written word I attribute to Norma Jean Anderson Shuler. Though a beautiful and busy teenager, she often took a little brother smelling of puppy dogs and bayou mud upon her knee to read Bible stories of adventure spiced with the enchanting magic of her love. What's seen here is merely one among tens of thousands of fruit-producing good seeds she has sewn through the years for the Kingdom of God. Finally, if one senses an apparition of a warm, dimpled smile within these pages, it is the osmosis effect of my good wife, Susie Marler Anderson. She's the fresh air this story breathes.

TABLE OF CONTENTS

ACKNOWLEDGMENTS

I wish to thank the many wonderful family members and friends who contributed the ingredients to make this story a blessing. These include my first-cousins Jerry and Jimmy Earl Brent, Greg Thompson, and Mary Ann Wilburn, along with Dale Poston. Distant in lineage only are Diane Tucker and Joyce McMakin. Sam Die refreshed sweet memories of the Harrison and Die reunions. In-laws Sandra Brockman and Nancy Anderson helped clear up some details of the NASA years. Too numerous to count are ex-Zestos employees or customers and old high school friends and neighbors. I heartily include two encouragers: Pastor Mike Allard of Crossroads Fellowship Houston and my boss-lady, Kristina Lindquist, president of Dynamic Products, Inc. I thank my editor, Melanie Saxton, for her encouragement and true appreciation of this historical account and her willingness to work on future projects. Thank you, also, to Holly Chervnsik of SuburbanBuzz.com Publishing for her patience and diligence in formatting the book, designing the cover and polishing the vintage photos.

FOREWORD

I met Johnny Anderson more than 30 years ago when I was serving as youth and children's pastor at Greens Bayou Assembly of God. In those days, it was more of a casual meeting, but in 2001 when I became the lead pastor, our friendship began to flourish. I got to know him and found he was a true Christian gentleman.

Later, Johnny would serve on my council of advisors, and I had the privilege of traveling with Johnny on several mission trips to Africa. I've watched him in meetings when times were tough and when times were not. He's one of the kindest people you will ever meet and a genuine man of faith and prayer.

When Johnny shared with me about writing this book, "An Inheritance Incorruptible," I thought, *What a great idea. This is something we need more of — the good ole days. We need to read the stories of what God did through those early believers.*

One of those faithful saints was his mother, Vida Mae Anderson. I called her "Sister" Anderson. She was a pastor's friend, and this title was one she carried with humility. A powerhouse of a prayer warrior and, as some would call her, "The Real Deal." She was a genuine 100% Christian. I believe it's this great godly heritage that Johnny draws from that gives him such insight into the early outpouring of Pentecost. He had to have sat around some campfires and dinner tables, listening to Momma and those early saints tell of the miraculous victories God wrought through their lives. These stories and struggles come to life on the pages of "An Inheritance Incorruptible."

This book is a must-read. For believers today, there is a

price to be paid, but the greater price was paid by those who went before. They did the hard work, and we are reaping the reward of generations of great men and women. That generation is gone, but if we will receive this incorruptible inheritance, we must get in step and set our face toward the prize.

Johnny gives the ingredients to receive that prize. Faith, prayer, determination and love pave the path to a greater future in Christ!

This is a beautifully written historical faith-based novel. I loved reading its pages. Enjoy the encouragement you will find within.

Mike Allard
Lead Pastor of Crossroads Fellowship, Houston, Texas
Author of: *Never Give Up!* and *Living In The Overflow*

FAMILY TREE

First, Second and Third Generations

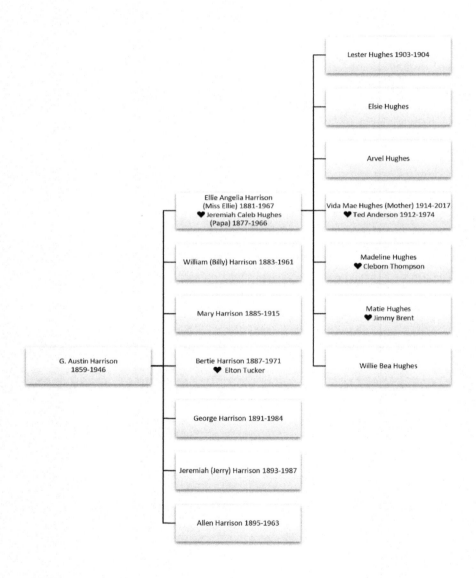

Lester Hughes 1903-1904

Elsie Hughes

Arvel Hughes

Ellie Angelia Harrison
(Miss Ellie) 1881-1967
♥ Jeremiah Caleb Hughes
(Papa) 1877-1966

Vida Mae Hughes (Mother) 1914-2017
♥ Ted Anderson 1912-1974

William (Billy) Harrison 1883-1961

Madeline Hughes
♥ Cleborn Thompson

Mary Harrison 1885-1915

Matie Hughes
♥ Jimmy Brent

G. Austin Harrison
1859-1946

Bertie Harrison 1887-1971
♥ Elton Tucker

Willie Bea Hughes

George Harrison 1891-1984

Jeremiah (Jerry) Harrison 1893-1987

Allen Harrison 1895-1963

Third, Fourth and Fifth Generations

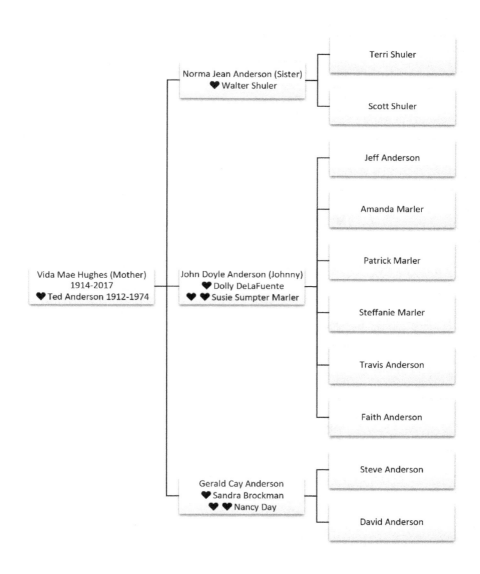

Third and Fourth Generations

Madeline Hughes ♥ Cleborn Thompson
- Greg Thompson
- Ronnie Thompson

Matie Hughes ♥ Jimmy Brent
- Jimmy Earl Brent
- Peggy Brent
- Jerry Brent

Elsie Hughes ♥ Dewey Wilburn
- Mary Ann Wilburn
- Buddy Wilburn

Arvel Hughes ♥ Della Jones
- "Billy" Hughes
- Edith Hughes

PROLOGUE

The inspiration to write this story came on the heels of the passing of my sweet, 102-year-old mother. It occurred to me then that something else of great value was on the brink of becoming lost, for she was the last of her generation in our family, and I'm one of the last of mine. Encouraging, captivating stories spanning over a century, timeless building blocks for an uplifting legacy of faith in a God who delivers His people through insufferable trials would fade tragically into obscurity if I fail to share what's been given in trust. I began this project, in part, as a tribute to our family name, but while recalling their remarkable stories and praying, my tunnel vision widened. The family name of Christian loomed larger, as the gift of Christ-based encouragement is transferred through these stories. It's too valuable to be hoarded by a few, for this family legacy is an empowering guide of proven truths. A guide that walks confidently out of the past to securely hold our hands now and into the future.

As 2020 and 2021 transgressed upon the spirits of folks everywhere, spreading a pandemic of fear along with disease and insecurity, I realized everyone needs encouragement to refocus on that which enables faith, hope, and courage. The enemy of faith is fear. Fear also blinds hope and steals courage. Since the Lord understands human nature tends to focus on fears — a.k.a. worries — we are commanded 365 times in the Bible to "fear not." Stories abound of famous leaders in the Bible and throughout history who understood the need to choose faith over fear.

Alexander the Great once learned that a cowardly soldier in his army was named after him. When asked, the soldier confirmed he was, indeed, named after his leader. The saying goes that Alexander confronted the soldier and told him, "Then either be brave or change your name!" Christian legacy-leavers understand bravery is good, but it takes something more. It takes faith in God. Alexander implied bravery is a choice, a choice required to represent his cause fully. The cause is tied to a name, and the name defines the cause and all who commit to it. With the good name of Jesus Christ, the cause is virtuous, and commitment produces a life of virtue. I've been emboldened in my journey by observing the bravery of those within these stories. They overcame crushing adversity by choosing the virtuous ways of Jesus.

How does one, I've asked myself, *encourage and inspire others to commit to such a cause and live virtuously?* The Bible encourages us with examples of ordinary people accomplishing extraordinary things who chose faith over fear and followed God's cause. People like David, an insignificant shepherd kid who became a giant-slaying king. People like Daniel who gave lions lockjaw. God worked amazing miracles in their lives, changing entire nations for the good of His cause.

But I never personally knew either of these wonderful old-time saints. Though their lives are still very encouraging, I sense that people today yearn to share stories of folks who are at least semi-contemporary, who face trials common to our own, and of whom we can better relate.

Those you'll read about in these pages are ordinary folks, the central characters I knew personally. I am one of them. The names of some characters have been changed, and a few are a fictitious blend of people I've known or real characters whose names I never knew. But the main events are true. Those events I've not personally seen were related to me by reliable and often multiple witnesses.

Oh, how I would love to hear them spoken again, as a boy sitting in my grandparents' farmhouse, snuggled down in Momma's over-stuffed parlor chair with the tantalizing smell of fresh-baked apple pie beckoning from her aromatic kitchen. Or absorbing the especially punctuated stories of God's power expressed with the unique vernacular of great uncles born to resolute country farmers in the late 1800s. I can see them still, their silvered heads nodding in unison, smiling crinkly-eyed faces looking exuberant and unjaded, joyously singing Gospel songs in between witnessing of His goodness. The fragrant, oxygen-rich air around them seemed to radiate love at our annual family reunions held in a tree-studded clearing next to Hickory Creek, deep in the piney woods of East Texas. The vitality of their character was as mesmerizing as their stories.

A pearly patina surrounds these vintage Christians in my memory. I aspire to be like them.

Our family stories speak of life through the most technically developed century in human history, beginning in horse-and-buggy dusty roads and eventually soaring through space in manned rockets. A common theme learned is that trials are a natural part of life. But for those whose trust resides in the Lord, it is during trials we gain wisdom of what's really important. Our priorities and our destinies are changed for the better. This is what I hope these stories convey to you, dear reader.

We've lived, loved, cried, and sacrificed. We've been burdened, been blessed. No one can claim perfection, and no one feels our lives have been lived in vain. We've endured by the grace of God, and because we have a great God, we hold forth a great hope. Some saw God work spectacular miracles through and around them; bombs-busting-in-air stuff. Others experienced more subtle miracles; deceptions reversed, unbelief enlightened, chains of fear removed, hurting hearts healed, and wandering sons reunited with their true destiny. These miracles happening within human hearts, responses from God to the prayers of loved ones and converging with His will, are no less profound in scope.

The rewards received by the committed faithful are worth all the troubles and toil and obstructions the common enemy of us all can throw at us, as our victory is assured in the name of Christ. Our reward is fitting as received from a loving Father who created all of Heaven and Earth. His love is as eternal as the gift of immortality. Our inheritance is indestructible, secured from decay or theft, subject to no degrading influences. For overcomers, it is our inheritance incorruptible. It's yours too.

Blessed be the God and Father of our Lord Jesus Christ, which according to his abundant mercy has begotten us again unto a lively hope by the resurrection of Jesus Christ from the dead, to an **inheritance incorruptible** *and undefiled, and that fades not away, reserved in heaven for you who are kept by the power of God through faith unto salvation ready to be revealed in the last time.*
~ 1 Peter 1: 3–5

Don't let the devil lick the sweet off your candy.
~ **Lucille Kelsey Gates**, *encourager supreme and treasurer of Greens Bayou A. G. For 37 years*
July 16, 1926 — May 19, 2017

Chapter One: An Extra Measure of Mercy

The two Texas-bred mules looked less eager than they had several days ago. Both now stared tediously downward with ears drooping as the endless dirt road passed swiftly under their bellies. Curbing the impatient urge to hurry on his desperate journey, 31-year-old Jeremiah Caleb Hughes — friends called him Cay — saw the signs of weariness in his mule team and reluctantly reigned them back to a slow walk. He couldn't overtax his mules now, for as the old country saying goes, "They are in it for the long haul." Cay was 100 hard miles shy of their destination, and the destiny of his family's life hung in the balance.

Eight days out from their West Texas farm in Floyd County, Cay rolled southeast while shading his troubled eyes with cupped hand against a rising sun. He couldn't chance missing any markers at the upcoming crossroads. They needed to stay true to course, for time was a critical factor.

Quickly getting to their destination was the only hope left, but that hope was like a faint light to a midnight traveler lost in unfamiliar woods — it was motivation enough.

Shoving off in a cloud of dust last week, Cay launched the 500-mile journey with a lustrous prayer and a bright hope. Even his well-rested and fresh-fed mules, Elijah and Noah, seemed to catch the spirit of Cay's faith-filled resolve as they vigorously thundered out of the barnyard with ears perked forward and mighty chests stretching the wagon's leather harnesses. But with each passing day, every new horizon seemed strangely more distant than the one before, and Cay's prayers held less conviction. Hot days, steep roads, and sleepless nights strained the endurance of man and mule alike. Hope's flame began to dwindle along with the mules' vigor while the sands of time dribbled relentlessly away.

Having taken an unfamiliar shortcut, Cay scanned the tranquil scenery of rolling green and fertile cornfields on both sides of the road, looking for landmarks to affirm he wasn't lost. He felt appreciation that the dry spell in the west hadn't hit the healthy crops here yet, as farming was in his blood since early childhood growing up in the Texas Panhandle. Cay was an offspring of God's good earth. He'd often sift a handful of fertile soil with as much finesse as a Tiffany's jeweler caressing a diamond bracelet. Cay's tired hands relaxed their grip on the reins, pulled a pouch from a hip pocket, and tucked a pinch of snuff behind his lower lip. The farm wagon's lurching slowed in cadence with the now-restful walking pace of the mules.

Cay also rested, relaxing his aching back against the wagon's bench seat while putting aside for a moment the heavy worries at hand. His mental and spiritual state needed a break too. He had driven himself and the mules non-stop, taking brief naps and food or rest breaks as needed to avoid a stove-up mule. His critically ill passenger was quarantined, and they couldn't use the modern steam-powered train system that crisscrossed the state. Mules and wagon were the only alternatives, making the wellbeing of both indispensable.

Cay decided to stop the rig and break out the water barrel. A dehydrated mule meant a disabled mule, which could tip the scales of life and death to an unbearable conclusion. He felt a sickening sensation in his stomach at the thought.

The slurping sounds of mules lapping from their water buckets lulled Cay into a meditative state. As a form of unconscious escapism, his overburdened mind reflected on sweeping changes taking place in his beloved Texas in this year of 1908.

Texas' signature industries of farming and cattle ranching had experienced some tough breaks lately. Abundant farm harvests from steady rains dwindled as a hard drought began in west Texas and scorched eastward, aborting crop production from the patched-britches sharecropper to the high-topped boots of cotton moguls. Farming capital dried up along with the crops, affecting Cay and his West Texas neighbors as farmland loans carried heavier baggage in rising interest rates.

Farmers were forced to look at alternative and unique plantings for the future. Always the agricultural knights in shining armor, researchers at Texas A&M University intensified the development of more resilient crop species. One notable A&M project was the successful grafting of advanced pecan sprouts into the tough native hickory trees for a hardier, more drought-resistant hybrid. Cay read that this should boost the newly-expanding pecan industry to help pave the way for less dependence on favorable weather patterns and keep rural folks out of the poorhouse.

But farming as a whole was on the brink of an inevitable downturn. Many squinty-eyed career farmers were hesitant to accept the industrial revolution steam-rolling their way. Generational tilling of the soil was a cherished tradition in Texas and one that did not fade easily. The expanding network of train tracks in the last decade, unhampered since the end of the Indian wars, was just the beginning. Old established pioneer towns dwindled if the railroads bypassed them. Along with the trains came modern manufacturing companies to build facilities and businesses unrelated to agriculture.

Cay was one of those who saw this evolution coming. He was troubled about his uncertain future these days, for he'd planned on being a farmer since he was six years old. Farming was all he'd ever known. He possessed a natural love for the land and the people of strong moral character forged upon it. Cay derived a deep satisfaction during harvest times from knowing his efforts provided life-giving nutrition to folks all over the state. He couldn't imagine feeling the same level of significance in any other vocation.

Jeremiah Caleb Hughes (mounted far right) with family at his childhood Texas farm, circa 1889.

Besides weather and agriculture, changes were occurring in the traditional usage of natural grasslands reserved for grazing beef cattle. This staple industry birthed the cowboy culture of Post-Civil War Texas. Grazing lands were leased out and trespassed upon by the scuffed boots of a new breed of human critter — oil-hungry nomads known as "wildcatters." Large pastures were being denuded of cattle while drilling rigs sprouted from the ground like campaign signs in an election year. Hard hats replaced cowboy hats in parts of the state, as there was more money to be made in the oil fields than in punching cows.

It seemed that the black bear of crude oil was raising upright on both hind legs to roar across the vast Texas landscape, while the old familiar gray-headed twins of ranching and farming held hands in a slow retreat.

Like many young Texans of his generation, Cay wondered if he could ever fit into such a foreign feeling industry if the well of his farm finances went dry. This was a high probability. Some local bankers, fickle by trade, used the drought as an excuse to forget their first love of family farms and pursue the new girl in town with petroleum-smudged greenbacks.

Bankers, oil companies, and outside investors made money as ranchers reduced stock and farmers suffered drought. Traditionalists saw their way of life threatened. One way or another, everyone felt the pressures of change.

Consequently, the wildcatters' rapidly advancing mechanized presence was welcomed by some and opposed by others. This controversy stirred the courthouse square of every one-horse town on both sides of the muddy Brazos. The topic of property boundaries and mineral rights replaced local gossip at the corner barber shops, as whole sections of land were opened to surveyors and geologists for oil exploration.

Some of Cay's neighbors embraced the changing landscape, citing a natural kinship to the wildcatters and linking the gamble of oil exploration to the pioneering spirit that flavored the souls of all true Texans. These folks had fireplace mantles adorned with mementos of family and neighbors lost in stampedes, historic floods, the great Comanche wars, and other perils of homesteading a wild and rambunctious land.

Others resisted the changes from the oil boom, basing their objections on general principles. They'd hook thumbs into well-worn suspenders, and with mustaches bristling, loudly proclaim those blasted Wildcatters so heavily rutted the rural backroads that they were useless as four-fingered gloves. Driving a hay wagon jostled the hat right off your head, and the tossing gave some folks a dose of seasickness. Sleep was a casualty, too. Mechanical noises from drilling crews echoed round the clock through the once peaceful cow pastures and hay meadows.

It was noted that many a farmhouse window slammed shut on warm summer nights while a long-john clad figure stomped angrily back to bed. This was often followed by muttering (with adjectives not heard in church on Sundays) that night sweats were better than suffering such ungodly commotions, which caused a farm's laying hens to cease production. Cay recalled a pithy hand-scrawled sign displayed inside the front window of a local general store that declared:

NO PEACE, NO REST, NO YARD EGGS TO BOIL. PATIENCE DAILY WE TEST FOR ONE WHIFF OF OIL.

Whether pro or con on the issues of rapid change, most old-timers agreed there hadn't been such an uproar since the Texas War for Independence against that old despot Santa Anna more than a half-century earlier.

***

One of the mules brayed a startling loud protest at a pesky green bottlefly buzzing his nose, snapping Cay out of these reflections. He reminded himself that no controversies took priority on this clear morning over the dire concerns of the last week. He was focused constantly on the state of his precious cargo. Time being critical, he resumed a grip on the reins and flicked them lightly, tapping his mules' backs to end the short break.

A faint moan behind him reached his sunburned ears.

Concerned for the quilted form in the bed of his weathered farm wagon, Cay turned to look at his supine passenger for the hundredth time since the amber fingers of dawn pushed the night stars off the eastern horizon. One glance revealed the loops of braided blond locks framing the pallid features of his beloved wife. Adjusting the cover with his free hand while holding the reins in the other, Cay realized with a chilling dread that the wagon bed smelled less like old hay and more like a hospital quarantine ward. It smelled heavily of decay. Straightening his trim torso and wagon-weary shoulders, Cay brushed aside the light brown shock of hair that habitually fell over his furrowed brow and ran a hand over the stubbled jawline. His hazel eyes and gentle features reflected the strain of constant worry.

There was just no denying it. His sweet Miss Ellie was dying.

A few weeks earlier, the elderly country doctor back home responded quickly to their summons for help when Miss Ellie took ill. After a brief exam, he removed his wire-rimmed spectacles, and with a regretful sigh, diagnosed her malady as the dreaded "slow fevers," better known the world over as typhoid. Cay's pretty Miss Ellie had possibly contracted it while serving as a midwife, attending to various ailments of sick folks in their county. No matter the time of day or night, she always answered the call for help when beckoned. Cay once sternly questioned his wife on the wisdom of exposing herself to the infections of others so often, as her nursing abilities and caring bedside manner became well known throughout their rural community, increasing requests for her skills.

Cay smiled for the first time in days as he remembered how she'd straightened her slight frame while untying that ubiquitous lace-edged apron (Miss Ellie loved to cook). With azure-blue eyes doing a war dance, she retorted, "Now Mr. Hughes, you know it's not Christian to ignore the sick and needy! I never have and never could!" Then her shoulders had relaxed as the roses returned to her fair cheeks.

That famous radiant "Ellie" smile that so enchanted him when they first met spread across her face, and in so doing, took all the starch out of Cay's resistance.

"And may I add, Mr. Hughes, that you're always quick to help folks whenever you can as well!"

He could only nod sheepishly that day in response to this charming retort. Cay knew Miss Ellie had been alluding to the fortuitous circumstances that compelled him to leave his home on the West Texas Plains and journey east across the state to the Piney Woods region where he was destined to meet the love of his life.

Family and friends picking cotton at the Die family farm in Tyler County.

This was where a local outbreak of influenza struck Cay's Aunt Donnie and most of her clan in Tyler County. The flu rendered them unable to harvest their ripening cotton crop, so vital to their financial survival. Indeed, the American demand for cotton was such that farmers all across the South referred to this lucrative crop as "King Cotton." Much like his compassionate Miss Ellie, Cay's immediate response was to join others in the western branch of the family as he hastily packed his Bible and other essentials before departing for East Texas, therefore setting out on his own odyssey of mercy.

That year was 1902, and Cay recalled first meeting several of Miss Ellie Harrison's family members at a quaint local country church, tucked away in a grove of picturesque towering pine trees near the town of Woodville. One beefy gentleman he met among the farmers and lumbermen sported the intriguing moniker of "Hurricane Jack" Harrison. Cay learned that Hurricane Jack, along with his very pleasant wife Lela, axed out a section of the Big Thicket woods several decades earlier near Menard Creek and the fledgling community of Votaw. The two settlers built a log cabin a few years after the close of the Civil War in an area reputed to have hidden a secluded camp of Jayhawkers. Those ne'er-do-wells hid in remote areas of Texas during and after the conflict and ventured out on occasion to commit sudden crimes on locals. But they left the young couple alone, for Hurricane Jack was young and physically very powerful at the time and confidently unafraid of any man.

Though soft-spoken and hospitable by nature, he had a reputation of blowing up like a violent storm when provoked. Hurricane Jack was not a man to be trodden underfoot by the lawless. He was known for saying, "I gladly humble myself before God, my parents, and my country. But there my short list ends." Cay took an instant liking to both him and Lela, inquiring more into their history.

The couple survived their remote homestead and flourished, raising a family while farming the fertile bottomlands and hunting the plenteous wild game of the region. Bears often killed their domestic hogs and chickens, so the Harrisons always welcomed parties of traveling hunters. Hurricane Jack gave hunters advice on the best areas to collect valuable bear hides, and Lela plied her ample skills as a nurse and midwife. She became known as "The Mother of Hunters" for her gentle nurturing to all who camped at their homestead and her tender ministrations to the sick or injured.

When Cay later met the pretty niece of these kind-hearted and resilient pioneers, he concluded that midwifery was more than just a necessity of the time and place. He figured that it was also a type of genetic blessing, that the Good Lord must have grafted in an extra measure of mercy through the generations of Harrison women…sort of like those hybrid pecan trees at Texas A&M University.

Along with a newfound love of the refreshing aroma of the region's pine trees, Cay found himself mesmerized by the warm and vibrant personalities of the Harrison clan. He fit right in like he'd been raised among them. They shared the same life values as his family. Those calloused lumberman and farmer's hands and unsophisticated garb that gave forth a bucolic first impression hid a quick wit liberally laced with good-natured humor. They laughed loud and often. Many were avid readers on a wide variety of topics, and conversation revealed a few were well educated, but none displayed even a hint of academic aristocracy.

Like Cay, they shared an all-encompassing love of their family, of Texas, of freedoms, and especially their Creator. The Good Lord provided all that they held dear. The

Harrisons displayed outward signs of affection to one another with a warm hug upon greeting and a gentle clap on the back before departure. Strangers were genuinely welcomed and made to feel at home within their circles.

This, then, along with a work ethic that demanded diligence in the stewardship of blessings received, was their enduring family legacy. Cay never seemed to have a dull moment when in their company.

While mingling with the crowd at a Sunday afternoon church social, Cay spied the lively and diminutive Miss Ellie. She'd just concluded singing lessons that she taught in the church house after services each week. Her lovely face held a natural perpetual smile, and her lighthearted manner proved contagious. Those around her looked as happy as kids at a birthday party. Though a full head shorter than most, her personality radiated an inner source of light that caused her to glow and outshine everyone else.

Miss Ellie's visage reached across the room and magically captured Cay's heart. He was instantly drawn to her like a June bug to a midnight campfire.

Cay shouldered his way through the crowd for an introduction. Bright eyes framed by a "peaches and cream" complexion (desired by country ladies whose sun-scorched cheeks often belied their youth) turned his way as Cay clumsily took the dainty hand offered forth. "So pleased to meet you, Mr. Hughes," said Ellie Angeline Harrison with a side-tilt of the head. A charming smile crinkled the corners of those exceptional, compelling blue eyes. "I've heard about you, and I think it's very commendable of you to travel all the way from West Texas to help poor Sister Donnie. Are you planning to return home after the harvest, or will you stay amongst us a while longer?"

Cay struggled to glance away from that captivating face for a moment and collect his wits. Only then could he formulate a proper answer. He had resolved to beat a hasty retreat the moment Aunt Donnie's fields were cleared, and the flu virus ran its course. He had commitments back home. One was the long-anticipated barn raising for his newly married best friend. Those were traditionally a community-wide affair, where construction of the new barn was topped off with some toe-tapping music from a good local band. Everyone would enjoy a buffet-style feast fit for a king, presented on a long line of outdoor rustic wood tables and lovingly prepared by the best cooks in the county. There was no way Cay could miss out on that, and he'd already told the neighbors to count him in before he set out for East Texas. Plus, he wasn't about to tarnish his solid reputation for careful planning and diligent adherence to those plans.

He was, after all, a very regimented young man. Miss Ellie might as well know this early on, Cay decided.

Squaring his shoulders, he raised his head and looked directly into those beautiful blue eyes again. Time froze to a standstill, and the active crowd surrounding them faded into a hazy vacuum. His firm resolve evaporated like morning dew before a bright Texas sun.

A realization flashed through Cay's soul that he'd never beheld anything on God's good earth quite so lovely as the perfection standing before him.

"Well, uh," he stammered, "Thought I'd hang around these parts for a while longer when we're through at Aunt Donnie's…and enjoy these pretty woods for a spell. And I guess I'll get to know some of these nice folks a bit better," he added awkwardly.

Oh well, Cay thought to himself that day, *There are times when a change of plans is a good notion.* His intuition, and his heart, told him that this was one of those times.

***

Miss Ellie and Cay were led outside onto the picnic grounds of the aptly named Shady Grove Church by her uncle, William Henry Harrison. They joined others sitting on patchwork quilts spread under the dappled sunshine and blue-sky backdrop above the towering sentinels of shagbark hickories, wide-leafed sycamores, and aromatic pines. Though the scenery was enchanting, Miss Ellie was even more striking sitting there in the sunshine. She held Cay's undivided attention and spoke highly of Uncle William, a big, burly, and bewhiskered elder who wore his wide-brimmed hat cocked slightly to starboard. His soft-spoken and kindly mannerisms contrasted sharply with the seemingly frozen stern facial expression carved upon his features by 40 years of hard East Texas ranching.

During the course of conversation, Cay learned Uncle William had the solemn distinction of being a first cousin to the late 23rd president of the United States, Benjamin Harrison; who was, in turn, himself a grandson of the 9th president and signer of the Declaration of Independence, William Henry Harrison — the ancestor Miss Ellie's uncle was named after. To Cay, however, Uncle William's most notable factor aside from a blue-blooded connection to national history was his obvious fondness for his favorite niece upon whom he bragged incessantly.

Uncle William confirmed what Cay already suspected about Miss Ellie's nature. Her sweet disposition and endless energy were often spent serving and attending to the welfare of others. She lived out the Christian commandments, and her love for the Good Lord was obvious. This quality of unselfishness combined with a childlike freshness of expression whenever she'd notice the simplest of nature's wonders endeared her to Cay in a way he had never before experienced.

Overlooked by others, tiny wild orchids with purple

blooms no larger than a dime sprouted by the picnic quilt in small clusters about three inches off the leaf-covered turf. Although she'd seen thousands like them, for they were prolific in Tyler County, Miss Ellie *ooh'd* and *aah'd* with girlish delight as she beheld their dainty charms. He loved her response to such a small and insignificant natural beauty. This facet of her personality enhanced her beauty in Cay's eyes.

Loving little things reveals a heart of big capacity.

He was so enamored of her that Cay knew a marriage proposal was already conceived in his heart by day's end. His previous plans were forever changed, and a short six weeks later, the lovely Miss Ellie became his bride.

***

"Mr. Hughes?" The feeble little voice from the wagon bed fetched Cay back to the present.

"Yes, Miss Ellie?" Cay softly answered.

"How long before we reach Shady Grove?"

"Don't you fret now, Miss Ellie," Cay replied in a gentle voice. "We'll be there before you know it. You just try and get some sleep and get well so we can enjoy that revival."

Cay turned on the wagon seat and smoothed the canvas cover down after tucking the quilt under Miss Ellie's chin. With dismay, he felt the burning cheek and realized that, unbelievably, the high fever was worsening. Substantially weakened by fever and the drastic loss of weight (unable to eat, she'd lost about 20 pounds), Miss Ellie struggled to raise up on one elbow to look her husband in the eye.

"Please hurry, Mr. Hughes," her trembly voice implored. "I heard Lester a'crying for his momma, and he sounds frightened. He's there at Shady Grove looking for me. I must go hug him in my arms and comfort him! And…" Miss Ellie tried to say more, but a strangling cough choked off her despairing words.

Suppressing the chill that flashed through his heart at hearing Lester's name, Cay tried to sound calm as he replied, "Now take it easy, Miss Ellie. I'll stir up these mules, and we'll be there real soon. Don't worry about Lester. Your sister Bertie is there, and she'll take good care of him until we arrive."

The answer seemed to pacify Miss Ellie. She closed her fever-glazed eyes and settled back down into the swaying wagon bed. Her bouts of delirium were increasing during the last few days, but she'd never hallucinated about Lester until now, Cay realized with rising panic.

Lester Hughes, their precious curly-haired little son, was born the year after Cay and Miss Ellie married and moved near the East Texas town of Warren. He was the apple of their eye. A chubby child with big rosy cheeks frequently dimpled with joyous laughter, Lester was lovingly doted upon by everyone. He especially loved being at Miss Ellie's side when she'd milk Emmy Lou, the family dairy cow. Lester would burst into fits of giggles as his momma occasionally squirted a stream of warm milk sideways onto his expectant little face. Miss Ellie would throw her head back in peals of laughter along with Lester as Emmy Lou looked back at the cackling duo with a lazy stare of bovine curiosity as if wondering what magic her milk evoked.

Cay took frequent breaks from working his fields to come inside on the pretense of getting a drink from the long-handled water pump in the farmhouse kitchen. But he was really just stealing a few golden moments to watch Miss Ellie play with Lester.

Those were some of the happiest days of Cay's life. Then at 14 months of age, Lester began one day to fret and cry a lot, which was uncharacteristic. By nightfall, he was feverish.

A few dreadful days later and one week after Thanksgiving, their little Lester died on the dismal night of December first, 1904, while a 'blue norther' cold front blew in, sprinkling frost over the frozen farm fields and through their numbed hearts.

Neither Cay nor Ellie was a stranger to grievous times or the tragedy of a loved one's death, but Lester's passing was the most agonizing ordeal of their lives. Miss Ellie wept uncontrollably during her nightly prayers and randomly throughout each day. Yet she'd bravely tell Cay everything was all right and that she trusted the Good Lord to get them both through the cold winter of their spirits.

Cay firmly believed in God and tried to live out the Christian life. But he'd felt weakened in his faith during this time. The ever-present question "Why?" kept echoing through his mind. For months he couldn't shed himself of the image of that wintry day in the old graveyard, where even the surrounding moss-draped trees had a natural lean away from its bleak aura. Cay constantly visualized the wind-swept granite tombstones looming throughout the graveyard like eternally silent harsh sentinels, bearing stoic witness as gloved hands lowered the pathetic little pine box into the cold, gluttonous ground.

A big chunk of Cay's soul was enclosed within that little box, and it too disappeared into the yawning cavity of an unjust grave.

"Why God?" Cay pleaded with tear-filled eyes sweeping a starry, moonless night sky hours after the funeral. "Why Lester? Why not me? Why not someone who's had a chance to know about living? Someone who's watched frisky puppies grow into lanky hounds and watch their wagging tails stir up a dust cloud when you get up early mornings and pet 'em. Someone who's planted seeds with their own two hands into good soil and watched 'em sprout and miraculously bloom, bearing plump vegetables or grain stalks or sweet fruits on green vines. Or swim in the cool water of spring-fed creeks on hot summer days with laughing buddies and hook cork-yanking catfish on cane poles. Someone who grins real big when blowing into milkweed tops as the barn cat paws crazy-quick trying to catch the scattered little white air-born seeds as they spin and flutter in the springtime sun…"

Cay buried his face in his hands as a broken heart finally stilled the rambling questions, and his words rose heavenward to take their place among millions of other lamentations throughout the centuries from fathers whose children were too soon taken.

The "why" of it all began to make Cay bitter, he realized a few weeks later, and the bitterness was preventing the healing peace of God that Miss Ellie prayed for so diligently. Cay began to search for answers in the Good Book, as he'd always heard the Bible was God's comforting word for man and a source of true wisdom. Reading scriptures early mornings and late nights while praying for understanding, Cay's resentfulness over Lester's death slowly dwindled.

While reading the Gospel of John, Cay began to accept that, though the "why" question of his little boy's too-early demise may never have a sure answer, both life and death are in the gentle hands of God. It occurred to Cay that even should he receive an answer as to why Lester was taken so young, it would not lessen his mourning or diminish the pain. An authentic love in one's heart for another cannot be stopped at will, even when that love finds a vacant address and the reason is understood. Therefore the pain of death's robbery of cherished life can't be ignored, nor instantly healed by the salve of reason. It dawned on Cay that God knew how severely his heart hurt over the loss of Lester. After all, God sent his own precious Son to the grave — but that death was for an eternally good purpose, and Father God understood altogether the "why" of the matter.

Cay's question was born from the pain of lost love. Revealed in scripture, God's answer was born from everlasting love.

God understood the whole scenario completely, and He mourned along with Cay and Miss Ellie. Cay had heard John 3:16 preached before, but the enormity of its concept began to unfurl like a giant scroll in his understanding. He now read it through the fresh perspective of a father grieving for his own son.

Tears blurred the scripture as Cay read and re-read, "For God so loved the world that he gave his only begotten son; that whosoever believeth in him should not perish, but shall have life everlasting." He began to understand that because of this gift, the death and subsequent resurrected life of God's Son, our son's lives may also continue forevermore, a real gift of encouragement for parents who'd buried their own hearts in a loved one's earthly grave.

Comfort was found in verses declaring an everlasting life follows earthly death that's temporary, as long as one believes in the Lordship and redemption of Jesus Christ. Scripture was very clear on this. Jesus' life was given not just for Cay and Ellie but for everybody in the whole world throughout all of time. This includes little toddlers like Lester, who've not yet reached the age of accountability, meaning not yet mature enough to decide for themselves the enormous issue of John 3:16. Cay's Bible revealed that all believers have great hope for renewed life, even in the grieving of life departed. And the bright light of that hope triumphs over the haze of pain and the limited reason of man.

This newfound hope in Cay parted the clouds of despair as the sun began to shine once again in his heart.

Later, in John 14:27, Cay read some of Jesus' last words given to his disciples before his crucifixion: "Peace I leave with you, my peace I give to you, not as the world gives, give I unto you. Let not your heart be troubled, neither let it be afraid." Cay meditated on this for a while. He concluded this was more than a precious promise of real peace to the believer. This was also a command — a command to consciously resist the troubling fears and bitterness that all people experience in life at some point in time.

As this precept grew in Cay's mind, he began to understand more that his life was bought at an extremely high price to Father God. There was purpose entwined in his life, and he could not waste it in bitter over-grieving. The recent events were an act of God, and if Cay were to trust in God's loving goodness, he had to accept that even those events that seem harsh for the moment have a resulting purpose that is best for all concerned.

Maybe if Lester survived, he'd have had some untold lingering suffering of mind or body. But Cay could only speculate. He thought of others he'd known in his lifetime that carried tremendous burdens for years after a serious illness. He'd witnessed how some forms of mental dementia tormented the afflicted and their family, day and night for years on end. Instead of nursing a broken heart, he purposed to change his focus.

Cay set his heart to completely trust in God, come what may, for the rest of his life. He took a measure of peace from knowing that Lester was enjoying the everlasting life with Jesus, for the Lord takes the very young who departs this world unto himself.

God's promises were enough to encourage Cay to carry on. No explanations required.

Though he'd be missed here for sure, Cay and Miss Ellie would one day begin eternity with Lester by their side. Cay shared with his wife that it was time for them to move forward while simply trusting God. Miss Ellie agreed. It was time to live again.

Now, Cay read his Bible for more purpose than to seek solace over Lester. He found himself reading for how he should carry on in everyday living, thinking, and planning ahead. He and Miss Ellie slowly began to heal and to laugh again. Her weeping spells were becoming less frequent. Hope was returning to their hearts as they'd discuss scriptures more than before along with the usual daily topics. They began to read the Bible aloud to one another, to pray together daily, and in doing so, found the bond of husband and wife strengthened. Their relationship with sweet little Lester may have been lost for a time, but Cay and his bride sensed that through their ordeal, an even more cherished relationship had been found with the Lord Jesus Christ.

Peace bloomed again in their marriage like a dormant rose taken from darkness into the light of day. The hurt wasn't gone, but peace diminished its paralyzing effects.

***

Winter was finally over.

Spring days brought mild winds rich with the sweet aroma of honeysuckle and new wildflowers wafting across the little farm. Every hillside and fallow field sported a thick carpet of lovely bluebonnets, daisies, verbenas, and other wildflowers made all the more abundant from the extra cold winter a few months earlier. This display was so easy on the eyes that Cay and Miss Ellie began to eat their lunch outside on a picnic quilt spread over lush new grasses. There was always at least one bouquet of fresh flowers in a mason jar placed beside them that Miss Ellie would gather for the day, attracting the occasional Monarch butterfly.

Every vein in his being sensed the tranquility of fresh life as it emerged before them. Cay was reminded of a poem by Henry David Thoreau. It dealt with beautiful fields of Ambrosia, whose fragrant mana gave immortality to the Greek gods, an immortality shared by men who partook of the experience. Cay imagined he and Miss Ellie inhaling Ambrosia's transforming air and nibbling its lush fruits.

Sometimes they'd see a momma doe with one or two spotted fawns gracefully crossing the fields towards the greening trees by the creek, as the local whitetail deer herd was in the birthing time of year. To accompany Miss Ellie's scrumptious "big as a cat's head biscuits," Cay gathered succulent wild honey that dribbled from several bee trees growing along the sandy banks of a nearby clear water branch. Arrowhead formations of wild geese dotted the blue sky at various altitudes, honking a cheerful farewell to Texas as they migrated to the northern lakes. Less blistering than in past years, the summer months arrived later with enough rainy days to keep crops flourishing and the usual powdery farm dust to a minimum.

Cay had surmised the Good Lord was giving them some extra blessings by providing choice weather to balance out the difficult winter just passed.

This notion was greatly punctuated late one summer afternoon as he was walking in from the fields. He heard Miss Ellie humming a favorite hymn extra loud as she strung her washing on the backyard clothesline to dry. She dropped her clothes basket and ran swiftly to him when she spied Cay coming through the white-washed wood picket gate.

"Oh, Mister Hughes! Better hold onto your hat 'cause I've got some big news guaranteed to put the wind in your sails!" she gushed excitedly with flushed face and sparkling eyes. Before Cay could get the question 'what?' out of his half-opened mouth, Miss Ellie impatiently exclaimed, "We're going to have a baby!"

After several minutes of whoops and shouting so loud that every chicken in the yard scurried, clucking and squawking under the house, the overjoyed couple knelt together to give tearful thanks and praise to their heavenly Father.

On March 29, 1906, a plump, red-faced baby girl, Elsie Jane Hughes, made her grand entrance into this world. The bright expressions of the fullness of life re-emerged upon the faces of Cay and his glowing wife. Later that year, Cay seized an opportunity to acquire a larger farm near some of his family in the West Texas town of Lockney in Floyd county. He loaded kit and caboodle into the creaky wagon, tied Emmy Lou to the tailgate, and with Miss Ellie holding baby Elsie by his side, pointed the trusty mules west and moved 500 dusty miles to their new home.

On August 24, 1907, a baby boy's birth cry once again echoed forth from the rafters of the Hughes family farmhouse. Arvel Monroe Hughes added blessing upon blessings as Cay and Miss Ellie saw a resemblance of Lester reflected in the little brother's face. If every smile were worth a dollar, the couple would've been millionaires by Christmas.

But, yet again, in this present hour, they found death once more encroaching upon them and upon the few years of abundant life they'd enjoyed after the time of mourning Lester's passing. Cay sent out prayer requests for Miss Ellie to family and friends everywhere and spent countless hours on his knees before the Lord, as close family helped with farm chores. However, his hope began to ebb as the hours turned into days after the diagnosis of slow fever, and Miss Ellie's health continued downhill. It didn't help that well-intentioned neighbors tried to make small talk by mentioning they'd heard of so-and-so's great uncle that had recovered from typhoid but was rendered blind or deaf afterward.

Accounts of the disease seemed to come to light more frequently, it appeared to Cay. One newspaper ran a story about the first wife of the famous western lawman, Wyatt Earp, who died of typhoid. Cay recalled hearing that President Theodore "Teddy" Roosevelt had experienced a crushing encounter with the disease. His mother died of typhoid only a few hours before his loyal wife passed away from kidney failure, both in the same house and on Valentine's day. After Lester's death and now with Miss Ellie's life threatened, Cay could relate to Mr. Roosevelt's diary entry: "The light has gone out of my life." Even a great man such as T. R. could take only so many intimate visits to the graveyard before the loss of life dimmed the heart.

When it became obvious Miss Ellie's condition was worsening, and the old chilling image of that dismal graveyard started waking Cay throughout the nights, a telegram arrived from Ellie's brother and Evangelist, Reverend Billy Harrison, back in Woodville. It gave Cay a reason to hope. He quickly made provisions for the family to watch the children as he prepared the wagon for departure.

Now here they were, riding the wagon on backroad shortcuts in a race against time, and in a crucial matter of life and death, with Miss Ellie in a delirium thinking little dead Lester was waiting for her. For a brief, surreal moment, Cay wondered if Miss Ellie's closeness to death had given her a glimpse into the hereafter world and that indeed Lester was waiting to soon have his momma with him once more. Was such a thing possible? Cay shuddered and regrouped his weary spirits, quoting to himself the scripture that Christians are to "...take every thought captive." With this in mind, Cay reminded himself, once again, that Lester was now in the company of the Good Lord. He would not be crying, as the Bible states, "there will be no tears or pain in Heaven."

Miss Ellie's fevered mind was playing tricks on her. Her fate would not be decided by any source other than God Himself. Cay renewed his conscious choice to focus on putting his hope and trust in God and that this attitude would dominate the thoughts of his mind.

Cay had wired Billy Harrison for prayers when Miss Ellie first became seriously ill, and Billy's reply was immediate. Remembering the telegram in his vest pocket, Cay pulled it out and unfolded it with one hand and his teeth, keeping the reins controlling the trotting mules firmly in his strong hand. The simple words strengthened his faith as he read for the umpteenth time:

> *Powerful camp meeting revival breaking out at Shady Grove. Souls saved and miracle healings. Bring Ellie post haste. Life is here.*
>
> *~ BH*

As Cay thoughtfully returned the crumpled telegram to his pocket, he heard a clamorous cawing directly overhead. Looking above the treetops, he saw a large red-tailed hawk soaring eastward and gaining altitude. With a wingspan of over four feet and a creamy underbelly contrasting the rusty-red widened tail feathers, he made a striking image against the light blue sky. A pair of shimmery-black crows flew close behind, darting left and right of the hawk in a harassing manner while squawking their harsh rancor. Yet, they kept a safe gap between themselves and the range of the hawk's powerful talons and beak.

"That hawk ought to be acting worried," Cay reasoned under his breath. But the majestic raptor looked neither left nor right at his would-be tormentors and instead appeared to be singularly focused upon his destination. It was as if the hawk had a clear vision of where he was going, and nothing would deter him. Cay's hopes began to soar along with the hawk while he intently studied the scene above. A connective spiritual thread emerged from this observation, evoking an analogy in Cay's thinking between his and Miss Ellie's journey with the specter of death hovering near and the hawk's flight alongside his evil-seeming adversaries.

At that moment, Cay recalled another scripture he'd read recently in the book of Proverbs, "Where there is no vision the people perish." *Miss Ellie and Cay DID share a vision,* he mused. A mutual dream of raising a big family in their own home warmed with the frequent laughter of playful children, healthy in mind, body, and spirit. A home where Cay could wash the day's honest toil off his hands and face every evening after working his fields, while the enticing aroma of supper cooking on Miss Ellie's stove blended with the sounds of her humming as the kids set the table. A home with a big window over the kitchen sink, where the setting sun's evening rays cast golden glows upon bowed heads and clasped hands around the table. A table where all gave thanks at every meal to the Good Lord for his bounty and grace and shared their daily thoughts and adventures as the bonds of family love grew stronger.

Cay thought of how often they'd spoken of this dream, this vision, and made a silent resolution to keep that vision strong in his sight. Typhoid or no typhoid, Cay determined to stay focused — like that hawk was doing.

Abruptly, as if on command, the crows veered away from their diabolic pursuit. Both descended in formation to settle in the upper branches of a dead cottonwood tree, still squawking in frustration towards the smoothly flying hawk. It was as if they'd finally perceived that the hawk's destiny was beyond their capabilities to destroy or divert him. The hawk flew peacefully on towards the rising sun.

Cay and family members in his farm wagon, circa 1910.

"Thank you, Lord!" Cay whispered. "May you deliver us from that which desires to destroy us like you just did for yonder hawk. And may we soar onward to the destiny of life you have awaiting us at Shady Grove…and beyond," he added prayerfully. Shady Grove, Cay breathed to himself, reflecting again on the last line of the telegram. Maybe that old hawk is flying there ahead of us. Maybe he believes, like I do, that Billy's telegram is true. That God's mighty power is working there, saving and healing his children. And that life is there.

Chapter Two: Miracle at Shady Grove

The midnight bell in the old mantle clock struck twelve in the small rectory at Shady Grove Church. A weary Billy Harrison dimmed the coal oil lantern by his make-shift bed. Along with his younger brother George, the Reverend Harrison had just concluded another incredibly moving night of revival, which most locals called a "camp meeting." Although he was exhausted both physically and spiritually, his mind kept reliving the heart-stirring sights of souls being saved, families reunited, and a few spontaneous healings that had occurred throughout the last few weeks.

Billy marveled once again at how the powerful works of the Spirit of God could change people's lives so suddenly and completely and heal their bodies so miraculously. It defied all medical and scientific conceptions of modern times. He had a fair knowledge of scientific concepts, having received an extended education and teaching school for several years before attending the famous Azusa Street Mission Revival in Los Angeles a year ago. He witnessed the unfathomable, supernatural power of God on a large scale there and several times since elsewhere. Every new encounter of this sort continued to amaze and invigorate Billy. It wasn't until after, never during, the 12 or more hours of steadfast praying, singing, preaching, and rejoicing within a revival that bodily fatigue came upon him.

Yet, however tired he was afterward, his soul was left elated and floating like one of those newfangled "lighter than air" planes that the Wright brothers revealed at Kitty Hawk. But even that powerful new invention paled in comparison to what God had been revealing to both Billy and George ever since Azusa Street.

Looking around the rough-sawn planks that constituted Shady Grove's sanctuary walls, Billy realized how much the rustic structure reminded him of the Azusa Street Mission building. Both were simply constructed of white-washed pine planking on the outside and had wide-open floor plans with no distinguishing architectural features. Except Shady Grove was only one story with a tall steeple, while the Azusa Street Mission had an upstairs area used for small sleeping quarters that doubled as daytime offices.

Those were the only significant differences — if one didn't consider the smells. Shady Grove smelled of fragrant fresh-sawn pine wood, as the church was fairly new built. But Azusa Street had a different history, previously as an African-American church and lately as a horse stable, among other short-lived business ventures in between. Those old dirt and sawdust floors were an aromatic collection of sweat, horsehair, musty grains, and a myriad of other similar substances best defined as "organics."

Yet the Spirit of God was so powerful in that manger-like building that miraculous evidence of the Creator of heaven and earth revealed throughout the Holy Scriptures became the daily norm. Billy wondered how many elaborate "upscale" churches and majestic cathedrals around the world could recall experiencing even one-tenth of God's powerful presence that moved in that unassuming ex-livery stable.

Opening the small window by his bed for some fresh night air, Billy stretched his five-foot-seven angular frame and removed his wire-rimmed spectacles before sitting down slowly to unlace his shoes. The cane-backed chair creaked softly, blending with subdued voices outside of families camping for the night in the wooded churchyard. He relaxed and let his thoughts drift back to when he'd first read about the Azusa Street revival in a local newspaper in the late spring of 1907. The small country school where he'd been teaching youngsters the "three R's" among other subjects, with chalk in one hand and a flyswatter in the other, was about to close for summer vacation.

Billy subscribed to several newspapers to keep his reading skills sharp while school was out. As he read various accounts of the reported spiritual happenings at Azusa Street, his interest escalated at the wonders those reporters must have witnessed. He always searched eagerly for these articles in a freshly printed paper, and his mind was never far away from the fascinating topic.

He didn't know then that he was reading his own future course and that the teacher would become a student of the miraculous.

Along with his brothers and sisters, Billy was a firm believer in the Gospel of Jesus Christ, and they faithfully attended a church of very conservative doctrines of worship. Church started punctually at the stroke of 10 a.m. on the Sabbath, and every family had their special place on the dark-stained oak pews. Floppy-hatted moms discretely, but firmly, finger poked the ribs of squirming boys, impatient and uncomfortable in store-bought leather dress shoes. Hatless men in starched white collars would turn their heads in unison as the preacher slowly entered the sanctuary, and with clasped hands and a slightly bowed head, made his way forward to step up onto the pulpit. The preacher was a very kind man that Billy admired.

Billy always sat attentively while the preacher solemnly read scriptures from an enormous black Bible and elaborated with lots of eyebrow-raising on various prophesies and scriptural interpretations. Some of the glorious accounts of God's miracles, such as the astonishing fire resistance of Shadrack, Meshack, and Abednego in Babylon's furnace, wrought a high tenor exclamation from the preacher that should have spurred a "Stand and shout praises to God!" enthusiastic response. Yet the best layman's reply was subdued, with only a casual "Amen" from a few elders on the front row.

This contrasted vividly in Billy's mind with the accounts he'd read of Azusa revivalists singing and shouting with such rejoicing that their praises were heard a block away. The vast differences in his church's reserved worship and the Azusa Street explosive worship blending with the awesome power of God displayed at every service intrigued him. Billy found himself wondering why such differences existed.

One difference Billy came to discover through his readings was the lack of hierarchical structure in Azusa Street. Billy's church had the pastor, an assistant pastor, various levels of deacons that held oversight of church business, a secretary, a bookkeeper, a half-dozen ushers, and other support staff, all serving a stable congregation of around 150 souls. This worked quite well, and common-sense orderliness prevailed over Sunday school classes, regular church services, and extra-curricular activities. Good schedules were planned and kept much like the public school system where Billy taught classes. He heartily approved of such a system. But contrarily, the Azusa Street Mission had just a few greeters, Pastor, and an assistant to the Pastor who doubled as secretary. Yet their attendees usually swelled to over 300 —and often many more — forcing standing room only with folks crammed shoulder to shoulder, frequently spilling outside onto the sidewalks.

More amazingly, Pastor William J. Seymour usually did not preach a prepared sermon but prayed and sang praises before opening a Bible to read scriptures. Then he sat on and behind empty wooden boxes in humble surrender. The revival services showed not the slightest bit of a human-designed planning, and therefore absolutely no evidence of the controlling hand of man. Worshippers, at random times, came forward to give a testimony from the heart or share a word of encouragement. Then the Holy Spirit of God not only led worship but swept through the crowded ex-stable and invigorated some to erupt with shouts of praise while laying others face down on the earthen floor in a physically overpowered state of awe.

One article penned by famed evangelist Frank Bartleman described his witness of a swept-aside religiosity and human arrogance by the mighty avalanche of God's presence, declaring that, "In that old building, with its low rafters and bare floors, God took strong men and women to pieces and put them together again... the religious ego preached its own funeral."

Billy surmised that when man communicated to man about God, a man-devised organization was needed to maintain order and efficiency, subject to the limitations of earthly beings. But maybe this system was unnecessary when God communicated directly via His Spirit to the spirit within the heart of man.

With every article read, Billy found himself excited to hear of folks experiencing a supernatural display of God's power. Yet, an undertow of natural human skepticism still tugged at his mind. Like most practical folks, Billy had grown up hearing the adage, "Beware of that which sounds too good to be true." Billy genuinely loved the Lord and fellowshipping and studying scriptures with other believers. Most of all, he loved seeing a sinner saved from Hell through the wonderful good news of the Gospel of Christ. But he couldn't help but wonder why God chose to be so physically and spectacularly active in that one small building in America, sparking not just a locally reported revival but a nationally recognized phenomenon. Was it possible that it was all just hype to sell newspapers, where a few well-answered prayers were overblown and sensationalized to appeal to people of faith such as himself?

There was one way to know for sure. Billy packed his bags and arranged transportation to Beaumont, where he'd buy a cross-country train ticket to Los Angeles and Azusa Street.

After two days and three nights at the Azusa Street Mission revival, Billy Harrison's life was forever changed. He wondered how in the world he could ever explain to George the intensity of power, of sheer love, of spiritual lightning as God's presence enveloped folks both inside that musty old building and even some passersby outside. Little brother George had wanted to accompany Billy, but prior commitments caused a delay. So "Little George," who towered a full six inches over Billy, wasn't due in Los Angeles for a few days yet. Billy pondered how to adequately prepare his brother for an encounter with the Almighty, such as neither they nor anyone else in the family had ever experienced. This was a challenge with no obvious solution.

Billy, at last, simply decided to let George find out for himself. Mere words couldn't do justice to the actual sounds of the rushing winds sweeping over and through several hundred people, sometimes laying them down in symmetrical waves like a wheat crop before a tornado-force downdraft. Nor could one describe the mutual awe as a 12-year-old boy, crippled since birth in both shriveled legs, was brought before the gathering. With voices raised in communal prayer, the child's crutches suddenly fell from his arms as he stood upright.

A thoroughly humbled Billy had blinked astonished eyes as the boy cried out, "Momma, look!" and ran a hand over his right shin. The previously pale and yellowed legs protruding from his shorts had turned a healthy reddish hue, and the stringy atrophied calf muscles filled out to a normal shape. Within minutes the gleeful lad was not just standing without his crutches but walking in figure eights before the rejoicing crowd. His weeping and ecstatic mother ran closely alongside with hands ready to catch her son should he lose his newfound balance.

The location of the famous Azusa Street Revival

The Lord had indeed healed her son, and he only grew stronger with each stride.

Billy had never seen anything like this. He'd witnessed the genuinely diseased and twisted appearance of the youngster's legs and had shaken his hand earlier, feeling the unusually heavy calluses built from the constant use of crutches. Beyond any doubt, he knew this miracle was not staged. Billy's unspoken doubts vanished for all time as his questions were answered. The ensuing praises and deafening shouts of thanksgiving after the boy's healing would've seemed like over-reacting in any other house of worship during regular services and certainly in Billy's home church.

But there was nothing "regular" about the astonishing wonders displayed in this service. Billy's voice raised along with the Azusa crowd. He saw and felt more evidence of the Holy Spirit, bona fide miracles and all, in three evenings than in all the days he'd lived. He watched in tearful joy as a jubilant Pastor Seymore picked up the lad's discarded crutches and placed them by the front door to join a stack of collected crutches, canes, metal leg braces, and other accouterments of the previously disabled.

Several other miraculous events occurred in the days and nights to follow. The consistent over-powering presence of the Holy Spirit was felt to such a degree that the visual appearance of miracles seemed almost a mere by-product of the revival. The power of God's love enveloped all in attendance to the extent there wasn't the least bit of division between the various races (of which many were well represented) or level of affluence.

Black, White, Brown, rich or dirt poor, young and elderly, male or female; all joined equally together in prayer and genuine affection one for another. The Spirit of the Lord had imparted to them the ability to see others in His true light. The old moldy societal norms, shamefully accepted for generations, dissolved. The attendees carried this new and refreshing outlook back to their hometowns.

To Billy, God's miracles were not just for the printed pages of the Bible anymore nor just for establishing faith in the early church's Christians, as some contemporary Theologians proclaimed. The God of Billy's day was indeed the same miraculous God of King David, of Daniel, and the Apostles. Yes, little brother George would just have to see this awesome truth for himself.

As Billy returned to his nearby hotel later that night, he decided that this kind of intimate relationship with the Lord was what he wanted for the rest of his days. He wanted to pray with more faith, sing more songs, and praise God more in every thought, word, and deed. He wanted to be more alert to God's goodness in both his fellow man and in the created universe around him. He desperately wanted to share more of the amazing grace of God the Father, the Son, and the Holy Spirit with others. He wanted to spread what he had learned, seen, and experienced. He wanted to give more love out to others, to testify of the great good news of the Gospel of Christ that saves souls for all eternity, to give and receive more of this life redefined in the bright light of absolute truth.

Billy prayed all of this directly out of his heart in a steady flow, without first construing the words in his head. He was only vaguely aware that his words were coming out in an unknown language. This had happened to Billy earlier during revival services in what some referred to as "tongues." During one service, someone spoke briefly in an unknown tongue while all prayed, and Pastor Seymour asked who had the interpretation. Billy was stunned that though he had not understood the words, he did understand the message, which was simply that the Lord would expand his Gospel of salvation through those present to many in faraway lands.

After Billy voiced this interpretation, Pastor Seymour later approached and thanked him for being sensitive to the Holy Spirit and explained that many of those who had the gift of interpretation usually received a call to ministry at some point.

Billy understood that tongues and interpretation were biblically described as a Baptism of the Holy Spirit. Though he'd previously thought this precept not conducive to modern worship, the Lord apparently had other ideas. In his private beseeching for more of the Lord, it was as if Billy was suddenly praying through a supernatural interpreter, for his natural language was too underpowered to convey the whole truth of his transformed heart. Though he did not understand the individual words he was praying, he fully understood the request. Billy simply wanted more of God in every realm of life. When the last of his prayer had cascaded forth from his lips, a spiritually overwhelmed Billy could barely speak the "Amen."

But as he did, in English, he realized two things with absolute certainty. One, the Good Lord heard his prayer, for the same awesome presence from revival was with him there. Two, Billy was a different man in many ways now, and he knew his church back home would not accept the new man. Their doctrine professed and believed in the supernatural described in the book of Acts but thought it confined to the early church only. Anyone declaring otherwise would be seen as antithetical to the modern church and politely ostracized from the assembly. Prior to his experiences with the power of the Holy Spirit at Azusa Street, Billy would not have easily accepted it either.

He now felt similar to someone in wartime who studied the mechanical workings of a modern high-powered rifle and even shouldered the piece and sighted down the barrel. But without actually pulling the trigger, there was no way to see and hear the muzzle blast and feel the jarring recoil throughout the body. Thus, there was no sure knowledge that an evil enemy had taken a hard hit from a projectile invisible to the human eye.

The trigger had been pulled in Billy's life at Azusa Street. He would now be on the front lines in the war between good and evil for all his remaining days.

It was then he received a Divine calling to preach. As Billy's "More" prayer was still pouring from his heart and a steady stream of tears dripped from his chin, he heard a voice call his name. In that small, dimly lit hotel room in a ghetto of Los Angeles and a few blocks from the Azusa Street Mission, God told Billy Harrison to return to Texas and preach the Gospel of Jesus Christ.

This, then, was the first news he gave an astonished little brother George when he arrived in L.A. After considering this for a moment, George inquired, "Well, Billy, are you sure it was the voice of God?"

"Yes, I'm absolutely certain it was," Billy said thoughtfully. "And it scared the dickens out of me and overwhelmed me with the challenge of it. I mean, I was so unsure of myself all of a sudden I blurted out my doubts to God by telling him, 'But Lord, I'm a teacher, not a preacher. I don't know how to preach! Why would anyone listen to me?'"

After a few moments of silence, George asked his brother softly, "Did the Lord answer that?"

During the conversation, Billy stared at his opened hands as if trying to decide if they were more suited to handle a stick of chalk or a preacher's Bible. He raised his head slowly and looked directly into his brother's concerned eyes. At that moment, George realized he'd never seen such a level of intensity reflected from Billy's face. Then Billy stated what he was to repeat often as a testimony of his calling for the next half-century.

"The Lord told me, 'You go preach my Gospel, and I will preach it with you. And they will listen.'"

Two days later, George Harrison also received a lifelong calling to the ministry of evangelism. The brothers would later learn that many were called during this extraordinary revival, including 38 missionaries who received their marching orders within the first five months of the movement. At Azusa Street's second revival anniversary, more than 50 nations around the world, including much of South Africa, had active Azusa-birthed missionaries boldly sharing the Gospel of Christ.

Billy's reminiscing about Azusa Street was interrupted by voices mingled with short bursts of barking from hounds outside his open window at Shady Grove. Looking out, he saw George attempting to help two others tie the lanky hounds to a hitching rail behind the church. He smiled upon seeing two characters entangled in a rope loop. One was a faithful revival attendee, "Big Willie" Davis, along with old Carl Mitchell (some referred to him as "Coon dog Carl"), a local character and semi-agnostic. One animated hound pranced about while pulling against his tether, encircling himself and the two men into one comical package. George tried to keep a straight face at the humorous mess and subdue the spasmodic dog long enough to unwrap the captives. He was not having much success with either.

Billy knew the men were hunting buddies who often set out late at night after their farm work was completed. Off they'd go with Carl's pack of hounds, hoping to collect a few raccoons before dawn. Their deal was to split the proceeds. Carl got the hides and Willie the meat. Most locals were glad to see them on the hunt, as raccoons were pesky adversaries to any farmer, able to destroy rows of standing corn in one visit while raiding henhouses to decimate eggs and chickens.

Many folks never would eat a 'coon, but Willie had a technique of first cooking off the heavy, strong-smelling lard that permeated the meat before washing and slow roasting the lean leavings with pork chunks. Those brave enough to sample the resulting dish were amazed at the transformation, and though it would never pass as a beef tenderloin, would confess to a grinning Willie, "This 'ain't half bad!"

Finally, the two friends were freed from the hound by the time Billy put his shoes back on and walked outside to join the little group. Billy knew that Carl had been hunting, for he'd earlier heard the hounds wailing as they struck a new scent trail. Plus, Carl had bits of leaves and twigs sticking to his clothing from running through the thick brush after the dogs, and his boots were crusted with creek-bottom mud.

"Well, Carl, did you finally decide to accept my invitation to join us in revival?" Billy asked tongue-in-cheek, for Carl's shadow rarely darkened the inside of a church house except for weddings and funerals. "You look well dressed for it if you have," Billy teased while plucking a sprig of cat-claw briar from Carl's hat. "And I know there's nothing like roaming around in the Good Lord's creation for a night to give a man a thirst for the Gospel!"

The men in the little group laughed good-naturedly before Carl, grinning sheepishly, replied, "As a matter of fact, Preacher, I was plannin' on moseyin' by here when I heard all that pretty singin' while I was down by Horse Pen Creek. But the dogs hit a good run, and I figured it was the Lord's way of tellin' me to keep on a'huntin', as Billy Harrison was probably yellin' about Hell and damnation, and he'd be pointing his bony finger right at me!"

Billy laughed along with the others as Carl began unstrapping his canteen and the cow horn he used to recall his hounds before shucking his deer hide hunting coat. As Carl flung his coat over a wood rail by the tethered dogs, a small and worn pocket-sized New Testament fell out. Billy stooped and picked it up. Turning to the flyleaf's short inscription written in flourishing sweeps of the pen, Billy read aloud, "To my Hunting Pardner Carl. Keep your powder dry and your nose to the wind. And may the Good Lord sound Heaven's Horn afore the devil gets you treed." ~ A. Steele.

As Billy handed the little Bible back to Carl, he said, "Looks like old Alfonso Steele has already done some pointing your way, my friend! And his finger aims a whole lot better than mine!"

Carl smiled broadly and replaced the book into a vest pocket; then, his voice took on a serious tone. "Alfonso is such a kind soul; a feller'd never figure that his shootin' finger has probly laid a dozen hombres in the dust. And every time they wanna keep honoring him 'bout San Jacinto, he jest tucks his old white-bearded chin down and says all them other fellers did the hard fightin'. Heck, everyone knows Alfonso fought alongside General Sam Houston and kept on even after getting shot. He didn't stop 'til the battle ended, and only then would he let 'em take him to Mr. Lorenzo's house to get patched up! But Alfonso's real careful to tell 'em it was the Lord that gave Texas that win over Santa Anna and saved his life, to boot!"

Billy was all ears and eager for Carl to continue. "Don't stop now! What else did brave Alfonso do?"

"Well, meeting him years ago over in Mexia, and us doin' some huntin' together's been a real good thing for me," Carl responded. "Alfonso told me all 'bout God and his son Jesus. At first, I didn't want to believe it all, but later I thought about it, and I told him somebody must've made these pretty woods and creeks and made the good in folks like him. That's when he gave me this here Bible, and he told me he ain't got a bunch more years left to work on gettin' the truth 'bout the Lord through my hard head. So, I said I'd read it. And he made me promise I'd pray 'bout it too…and I have."

"That's a fine testimony," said Billy. "And how did Alfonso's advice settle in your heart?"

"In a way, I reckon I do believe there is a God now. But I confess some doubts are a'lingering," Carl added almost in a whisper as if speaking more to himself than the small group of men.

George had been listening intently to Carl's story and asked, "Have you seen Alfonso lately?"

"No, not in a few years. But I hear he's still livin'," Carl replied.

"Well, I just read that Alfonso Steele and one other veteran of the Battle of San Jacinto are invited to speak at the next session of the Texas Legislature in Austin!" George exclaimed. "I think they're the only two still living."

"I don't doubt it. Alfonso was 'bout 60 years old when we met at a hound breeder's home. We got invited on a hunt together," Carl answered. "That was over 30 years ago, so I'm sure he's well in his 90s by now. And he's a humble man. I knew him several years before I found out he had fought at San Jacinto! When I kinda got on to him 'bout not lettin' me in on this, he just said, 'Well, son, I am proud of Texas gettin' her freedom after San Jacinto, but I ain't proud of the men I killed that purty spring day. I had to ask the Lord's forgiveness ever' day fer years after afore I felt better 'bout it."

Carl stroked the ears of his youngest hound for a few moments while he seemed in deep thought. "That's when I first asked Alfonso if he really believed in the God folks pray to on Sundays, 'cause I weren't sure there was a God. I'd had some mighty rough goin's in my early years, and I figured a God like I'd heard 'bout in church as a youngin' wouldn't let such stuff happen."

Carl paused a moment before he continued, grappling with the return of old familiar sufferings of loneliness and rejection, stirred up like a bitter gall by the memories of his youth. "Like when my pa died all of a sudden, and shortly after that my little momma got killed and throwed in a vacant field like she was so much trash. Them that did it never got found out. After her funeral, my kin told me they was a sellin' the house, so I had to git out. I was 18 years old, and it felt like my whole world had burnt up. All I could do was sit under the lightenin'-split sycamore tree next door, and hang my head while I cried out a river one minute and pounded the ground with my fists the next. And I wondered to myself that day, if there was a God, then where was he?"

Gazing down at the pup he'd been casually petting, Carl noticed it cocked its head sideways, quizzical as if listening to every word. "Guess I've been a wonderin' that ever since," Carl finished with a forlorn sigh.

Willie quietly took in the conversation with a thoughtful look on his face. Leaning back on the wooden hitching rail, he stuck both hands in his trouser pockets and drew in a deep breath, deciding to speak his peace. "You know, Carl," Willie began, "You and me done talked 'bout lots of stuff through the years while huntin', but not much 'bout the Lord." He let those words drift in the night air a moment before straightening up, stepping away from the rail, and putting a hand on his friend's shoulder.

"These last few nights here at revival, I been prayin' with folks, prayin' for folks…and prayin' for you, Carl. Mr. Billy's preachin' done stirred up a heap of concern in me 'bout what'll happen at the judgment day. Them words he speaks on what Jesus done at that cross, and why he done it, has got first place in all things important. Ain't no way me and you is gonna keep outta Hell less'n we repent of them sins that we all have in us since Adam and Eve went against God!" Willie declared with a jerk of his head. "We can't get it outta of ourselves without surrenderin' our life to Jesus by believin' in him like the Good Book says. Our sins are like bad fat that's just natural growed in them 'coons. But only the blood of the Lord can wash it out and make us clean for to be let into heaven."

"Amen," George said softly. Billy followed suit, his heart warmed by Willie's words.

"Now God is real, old friend, and He knows what bad happens to us," Willie continued, "and he loves us through them things. Ever since sin came into this ol' world, bad stuff is gonna happen, but the Good Lord tells us to walk with faith in Him through it all, and He has promised us a reward forever more if we do. You gotta trust Him even though you cain't see Him, jest like you trust them hounds to smell out a 'coon even though you cain't see that scent trail. But you know it's there somewhere. And you 'spect them dogs to keep on a'goin', even through the briars and the big logs and trippin' vines until they trap that coon up a tree for you. And when they do, you love on 'em and give 'em some good food and cool water and a soft place to lay down to rest when the hunt's over. God loves us a bunch more than you do them faithful hounds."

At the mention of his beloved dogs, the corners of Carl's mouth tilted upwards somewhat. "Maybe you shoulda been a preacher, Willie," he said.

"You know Carl, maybe I should've. Lord knows I got plenty of stories. My daddy, you know, was born a slave, and both he and my momma lived their early years in slavery. It was a very hard life and full of troubles and grievin' at every turn of the road. Even when they was freed they hardly ever had enough food and clothes to go 'round for me or my baby brothers and sisters. Our old shack was terrible cold in the winter, and we slept in sweat most summer nights. But my old daddy never complained. He just worked any job he could get and he always declared that he warn't worried. He'd always say, 'The Lord takes good care of his own.' Daddy declared he was free in the best way; free in his spirit 'cause his soul was in the hands of God. He said slavery of the spirit was the worse kind 'cause it steals away hope; and that's why slaves would sing while a'workin' as them purty songs sorta freed the spirit for a time. He told us the Bible says that where the Spirit of the Lord is, there's real freedom. And that real freedom is reason we have real hope."

"That deserves another Amen," interjected Billy, profoundly touched by Willie's account of faith amid adversity. He could learn a thing or two from wise old Willie, a man who shared the same faith despite walking a path infinitely more difficult than his own.

"Then when I got old enough to learn how to hunt, daddy told me somethin' 'bout a good dog that I ain't never forgot. He said to me, 'Willie, a good dog is the onliest critter on earth that will lay his life down for his master. And he'll do it without no hesitatin', too. With no thought fer his own well bein'. If a bear or boar-hog was to rush you, that faithful hound will throw hisself right at 'em, even a'knowin he can't win; just to protect you. He'll give up his life just so's you can be all right. Well, that there is what our Savior done did fer us, even afore we was born, and even without us askin'. Even if we is slaves and some folks treat us mean, or we is freedmen in this world, it don't matter to Him where we rank among men. His faithfulness and sacrifice makes us freed, no matter what man says, and no matter what troubles may burden us, and his faithfulness can be trusted.' Now you remember that, son."

"I'll remember," promised Carl.

"Well, more than promisin' to remember, can I get you

stay here with us a few days and listen to the word of the Good Lord so you'll understand what you gotta do?" Willie asked. "I'm askin' you as your friend. I been prayin' fer your freedom. Slavery been outlawed a long time ago in this country, but you in chains anyhow. I want you to find freedom from your past, and to find a reason to hope again. Keep them hounds at home fer a few nights, and please join us here in worship and prayer, so's you can join us in heaven fer evermore," Willie concluded through a whisper as his eyes welled with tears.

Carl, profoundly moved by Willie's stirring plea, hugged his good friend tightly for a moment before sitting back against the wood rail with shoulders slumped and head bowed. Twice Carl started to say something, but a catch in his throat prevented him from doing so. He seemed to be in a tug of war internally. The other three men could sense his struggles as he battled within to accept Willie's invitation or continue to avoid coming to grips with God. That scared and hurt teenager from decades ago still held tight to the chains of doubt.

Carl abruptly raised his face, now flushed with emotion to inquire of Billy, "Preacher, what was it y'all was singin' earlier while I was in the woods? It was the last singin' jest before I heard everbody fold the chairs and wrap up fer the night. It struck me as the prettiest singin' I ever did hear, kinda' like angels might sing. And that's when I blew the horn to call the dogs back so's I could come to the churchyard."

Billie glanced at George, who pulled his Bible from the front pocket of his coat and handed it over. Their eyes met in a mutual understanding of the significance within the scene transpiring before them. Billy thumbed quickly through to the Book of Acts before replying to Carl, "Well, sir, we've been discussing something that happened to the Apostle Paul when he was locked in a prison with Silas. The

47

Lord sees all things and can deliver anybody from any tough spot at any time and from any prison, whether physical or spiritual. In this fact, the believer has a blessed assurance that God does not leave his children alone. We were singing that truth. That "Blessed Assurance" hymn was a tribute of praise unto our Savior, and as a way of rejoicing in song, for we are an heir of salvation as the lyrics state."

"Yep, that's it," said Carl. "A mighty purty song."

"You heard how loud we sang earlier tonight, especially the verse 'Perfect submission, perfect delight, visions of rapture now burst on my sight, Angels descending, bring from above, echoes of mercy, whispers of love.' That might be the parts of the song you heard best," Billy stated.

"That's what I heard, all right. And I sure wanted to sing along and belt it out, too! But then, I ain't ever had no visions of anything so good as that, nor been shown any mercy or real love since momma died. Whoever wrote that song must've known such things, though. Yet it's one thing to write and sing about such sweet things, when you get to live and experience it. But I cain't see how someone like me who's lived with hard turns in the road could ever sing it so good like ya'll were doin'."

"Let me get this straight, my friend," Billy softly began while brushing some dust off his coat sleeve with short flicks of his hand. "You can't quite see yourself singing praises in a true spirit of joyful thanksgiving for God's love and mercy. And the reason is because, unlike the author of 'Blessed Assurance' who must've had an easy life to write such a song, you've had a lot of tough breaks that blind you to God's assurance. Carl, you're an heir to His treasures of mercy and enduring love, yet somehow you doubt it?" Billy ended the question as he settled back against the hitching rail, his hands now clutched together and eyes raised to look squarely at Carl.

"I reckon you got it right," Carl said, slightly puzzled and with a hint of defensiveness as he wondered where Billy was going with this.

"Carl, singing praises about His goodness isn't limited to folks who're exempt from life's tragedies," Billy said emphatically. "People who compose these songs aren't overly devout due to the absence of suffering. Quite the contrary. Many of our best-loved old hymns were written by broken people who suffered immense loss or terrific hardship. But they endured through the storms of life by obediently trusting in God, and in turn, received an unexplainable peace that compelled them to share this spiritual experience through song."

Carl tried not to look too skeptical.

"What a Friend We Have in Jesus" was written by Joseph Scriven," Billy continued. "His fiancé drowned the night before they were to be married. He fell in love again years later, and she also died before they could marry. And "Amazing Grace" was written by an ex-captain of slave ships, John Newton, who for years carried a heavy burden of guilt for his part in the shameful atrocity of man's enslavement of his fellow man. Oh, and let's not forget Frances 'Fanny' Crosby. While still a very small child, her daddy died, her mother abandoned her, and her grandmother raised her. This extraordinary and totally blind lady wrote "Blessed Assurance" back in the middle 1800s. She could see far beyond what many of us healthy-eyed folks grope to find."

Now it was Carl who was all ears. "Them is some sad stories, all right," he said with a nod.

"Yes, indeed," agreed Billy. "So, my friend, it's not what happens to us that determines our destiny, our outlook, our freedoms of heart and mind, nor our state of peace or lack thereof. It's a matter of *who* has happened to us." Billy spoke these words not to win a debate but to share the light of an incorruptible benevolence to a fellow human struggler blinded by the darkness of spiritual adversity.

"You seem to be seeking the next very important step in your life, Carl; a step towards a decision everyone must make at some point in time. And that is, what will you do with this Gospel of Jesus Christ? Do you accept his atoning death on the cross that redeems you in the eyes of God by paying your sin debt? Or will you reject this promise from a loving Christ, and therefore reject God, based on the injustices and human suffering in this world that seem to defy the existence of an all-powerful, loving God? Our human eyes can see worldly injustices, and though we can see the amazing and complex creation around us, we cannot see God. But this is in no way proof He doesn't exist. I pray and hope He will reveal himself to you in some way, as you need him now more than you know. And you need his blessed assurance of life hereafter."

At this point, Carl's face softened, and he looked less skeptical.

"Without this blessed assurance, what can a man hope for after the struggles of this life are over and he takes his last breath? Only a bleak and dismal nothingness? If that's it, then our current lives are absolutely meaningless. It's either one or the other, Carl. We all seek to be freed from the bonds of indecision, the bonds of doubt about what the human eye cannot see but the human spirit inherently longs for, as we were created by God with a yearning for a deity in our hearts that only Christ can fill."

George took a step toward his brother. "Billy, those are powerful words. And I'd like to add some thoughts too. Many of us Christians have experienced some doubt about the reality of who and what God is or is not at some point in our lives. Carl, part of my reason for traveling all the way to California, like Billy, was to see the Azusa revival for myself. The newspapers we all read talked about the miracles. And my brother Billy, here, observed some works of God that seemed to border on the miraculous but could have had explanations that contradicted a supernatural act. Well, I saw the supernatural actions of God at Azusa Street firsthand. Though my doubts have been dispelled forevermore, I understand your predicament. I do still have some wonderings of my own, but they are mostly the result of one absolute fact: no human can ever fully understand the perfect workings of God Almighty."

"That's true," agreed Billy. "And I haven't come to a reasonable answer as to why evil exists to such an extent as we see in this old world. I'm sure God could stop it, but He allows it, at least for now. I can't help but think God has a perfect purpose for this, and just maybe it's so his goodness will shine so much brighter as a contrast to evil. Or maybe even that it serves as an option to use our God-given free will, to choose either one or the other of two ways of living this life. He does tell us it is but for a time, and he will make all things right at the appointed time. I, personally, take some comfort in this."

"Preacher Billy and Preacher George, here, is tellin' you this out of pure love," interjected Willie. "I ain't pretendin' to know it all, but I have faith anyways."

"Thank you for that, Willie," said Billy. "And along these same lines, I do not know why all prayers offered do not result in the miraculous healings we see at Azusa Street. But even there, some were prayed for with no instant or obvious result, though most were healed. Maybe it's found within the amount of faith in the heart of the afflicted or in those offering the prayers? I can't say for sure, though I do know that faith is a very necessary element.."

"I done wondered about that myself," admitted Carl.

"Yes, why God sometimes chooses to perform a miraculous healing as a direct, timely response to intercessory prayer, and why He does not do so at other times, is a commonly asked question." Billy paused a moment while glancing at the Bible in his right hand before continuing. "The Bible states many times that man cannot understand all of God's ways as His thoughts are far above our thoughts. Even the Apostle Paul, who wrote so much of the New Testament, was denied healing of some undisclosed ailment. God told him, 'My grace is sufficient for you.' I take that to mean that God is telling Paul that this ailment, though burdensome, would not hinder his carrying out his life's purpose. Though only a partial answer, it leads us into a train of thought that merges with the personhood of God."

"That's it!" exclaimed George. "Just like Willie said, we have faith even when we don't fully understand."

"Absolutely," agreed Billy. "What we can understand is that every decision and action of God is for his purposes, which are always for an everlasting good. That's just something a man living in the finite world has to overcome when trying to comprehend the reasonings of a God who exists in the infinite. We can accept this fact without having proof in some form of man's limited-dimensional science. There's enough evidence for anyone who will truly look without any bias for the existence of God. This is the basis for believing in His Word as absolute truth."

"You use some mighty big words there, Preacher Billy. But I'm listening," responded Carl as Willie and George let loose some good-natured chuckles.

"I supposed I'm guilty of that too," declared George with a wink at his brother, "and thank you, Carl, for pointing it out."

"Well, yes, I guess teaching science in school has something to do with it. I enjoy it as a subject of study. And by the way, some of the theories and 'facts' have been found defective as new discoveries emerge throughout the centuries. They have to rewrite scientific journals and textbooks on occasion. So, we should never surmise — er, *assume* — that science is the ultimate revealer of facts. The Bible does not require such correcting, as it is an account of truth, written by men as instructed by the Spirit of the One who is the embodiment of truth. Many biblical stories of historical events disputed by the scientific community are proven to exist. Modern archeological digs are finding relics of cities and cultures that substantiate — er, *support* — biblical scripture."

"You get an A for effort there, teacher," said George with a grin. "But I think you and me both need to practice on our delivery."

"Apologies, Carl. I pray that over time I become a better preacher. I have faith that I will grow in this role. And I have faith that you will be grounded in more than just random scriptures or even the testimonies of your trusted friends. In the book of Exodus within the Old Testament, there's a point when God sent Moses to free the Hebrews from 400 years of slavery under the Egyptians. But when Moses tried to explain this to the people, the scriptures tell us, 'They hearkened not' to this message from God because of 'anguish of spirit and for cruel bondage.' I feel that you also have a certain anguish of the spirit from past hurts."

Carl looked to Willie and George, and then back to Billy. "I reckon there's some truth in that," he replied.

"Well, Carl, please don't let this wall of anguish prevent you from hearing what your loving God is trying to tell you. Maybe you'll need to hear the very voice of God speaking to your heart for your faith to become anchored in solid ground. Maybe you'll need to witness the supernatural actions of our God, perhaps a miracle healing at some point in time."

"Whew, wouldn't that be something else, Carl!" exclaimed Willie. "When you see it with your own eyes, ain't no denying it."

"Truer words were never spoken," Billy agreed. "I've been extra-blessed to have experienced both, and why God let me see miracles and hear his voice, I do not know. But He did. And He gave me this mission in life, which is to do as Jesus did and reach out to seek and save the lost. Those who are lost in indecision, lost in the dark clouds of deception, lost from the true way of life everlasting — these are children of God who find their way back to their Father. Let's do some searching in the Good Book."

Carl intently listened as Billy read aloud Acts 16:25 and 26 and then cleared his throat. Quickly glancing at Carl, he said, "Remember now, both men in these scriptures were in a terrible, miserable Roman prison with shackles on their feet, and their backs bloody from just being beaten within an inch of their lives. Their future looked very dim, and both had plenty of reasons to be afraid. Many folks in such a spot would naturally wonder where God was and why He wasn't helping them. But here's what these men did: 'And at midnight' (Billy looked at his pocket watch and glanced meaningfully at Carl, for the time was only 30 minutes past that hour) 'Paul and Silas prayed and sang praises unto God: and the prisoners heard them. And suddenly there was a great earthquake, so that the foundations of the prison were shaken: and immediately all the doors were opened, and every one's bands were loosed.'"

Carl was silent but wide-eyed.

"Now Carl, old buddy," Billy continued, "I know you've seen the wonderful changes in the lives of many folks around here, including Willie, when they surrendered their hearts to the Good Lord. Lots of folks at this revival have led lives of hardship but have chosen to stay in prayer and sing God's praises anyway. Like loyal Paul and Silas did. Let this witness of all them, along with Alfonso Steele, Willie, and me, for that matter, help you shed yourself of the doubts of Satan, the old enemy who wants to keep us in shackles. It shouldn't take an earthquake to get you freed…"

Billy's words came to an abrupt halt as a deep rumbling sound broke the still night air. All four men in the little group reflected a quizzical wonder as Willie ventured, "You know, maybe Mr. Billy just prophesized! Cause that sounds mighty like an earthquake to me!" A few tense moments later, his eyes narrowed as he added, "Or maybe some crazy fool is a'whippin' horses over those big wood timbers across that washout up the road!"

Long logs harvested to use building bridges over creeks. Some members of Harrison & Die family among the logging crew. Circa 1910

Widening his eyes, Cay tried to see the darkened dirt road beyond the short circle of light thrown forward of the galloping mules. The little Bullseye lantern mounted on the wagon flickered a weakened beam as the depleted coal oil level barely soaked the wick. Both mules were heavily lathered and thrusting forward with mouths open, gulping huge intakes of air while their lunging hooves pounded the red clay road. Half-crouching on the bench seat of the wagon and peering intently into the blackness of the midnight air, Cay snapped the reins onto the backs of both mules and strained to see the branched cutoff to the north that would take them the last few miles to Shady Grove.

In full panic mode now, almost shouting as he prayed aloud to God, his words stumbled over one another. Cay begged for mercy and promised devotionals and praises offered upon every hour of every day — if only God would spare his precious Miss Ellie.

At the last stop to rest the exhausted mules, Cay could not awaken Miss Ellie. Her opened mouth emitted faint ragged breaths that signaled she was tottering on the edge of death's bottomless sinkhole. Cay gently thumbed her eyelids to expose and perhaps awaken her, hoping against hope that he could bring her back to consciousness. Those eyes used to look at him so adoringly but now rolled slightly upward, unfocused and unseeing.

He had seen folks die before, and there was no doubt that Miss Ellie had but a very short time left — and maybe no time at all. With a frustrated cry, Cay threw a box of clothes and a piece of leather repair hardware over the side to lighten the wagon. Then he turned in his seat to snap the mules into a full gallop.

"Hold on, Miss Ellie! We're almost there! Your brothers and Bertie and everybody will be so glad to see you! Please stay awake, sweetheart!" he exclaimed over his shoulder, using the rare endearing name for Miss Ellie that he had uttered upon her birthing Lester. A quick glance back revealed no response at all. According to the wagon's motion, Miss Ellie's head swayed to the left and right, much like people did when shaking their heads "no."

"We can make it! We can make it!" Cay proclaimed aloud to himself as much as to Miss Ellie while the road dust billowed up behind the racing wagon and drifted into the dark and foreboding piney woods.

Ellie, however, did not hear those words, nor was she aware of the dark night enveloping them. She was seeing in her mind's eye a scene from several years earlier. She and her lovely sister Mary, along with her younger brothers, worked in the family field behind the two-room farmhouse, hoeing weeds out from between the straight rows of cotton. Sister Bertie was in the house, helping their momma cook supper. Mary had secretly snuck out of the house the night before as their father laid in a drunken stupor, directly after refusing her request to attend a traveling revival meeting nearby.

She'd heard from friends about the revival, and Mary thirsted to learn more than just the basics of the Gospel. She decided to risk her father's wrath and attend for at least one night. Their father thought church meetings were a waste of time and forbade his children and wife from attending to hear "pew-jumping preachers blather about an invisible god." They were to remain home and attend to the rigorous chores of farm life.

Their father was a hard task-master and a harder drinker. All the children felt sorrow for their mother, who endured a life devoid of mirth or hope, suffering not just physical abuse but some mental issues as well for an unknown reason. But Mary was the courageous one, and she'd heard enough about Jesus Christ from friends and other family members to whet her desire to learn more.

So that sunny day in the cotton field, Mary gathered Ellie and the boys to tell them about the revival. She excitedly explained the story of God creating the world, then Adam and Eve, and how their perfect existence was ruined when they chose to disobey God, thus releasing sin into the world. She spoke of Noah and the Ark, David and Goliath, and Daniel in the lion's den. And she told them about the Lord Jesus Christ, how he came to the world at the command of God to save everyone from sin and sin's penalty of Hell by giving his own life upon the cross. Mary cried when she told them she'd given her life to Jesus at that revival and that she was saved.

Then she took off her sunbonnet and drew a circle in the field's dirt with her hoe handle. Mary told them with a trembling voice, "If you want to be saved and you believe that Jesus Christ died to pay your sin debt so you can go to Heaven instead of Hell, step inside this circle!"

Ellie and her brothers looked briefly at one another, then nodding in unified agreement, all stepped simultaneously inside the drawn circle. Mary had them join hands, and Ellie could hear herself and her brothers praying. As the scene started to shimmer and slowly fade in Ellie's fevered mind, she could still hear Mary's voice saying, "We can make it to heaven now! We can make it!" Mary's last few words began to sound strangely like Cay's, but from a far distance.

As those voices and the scene blurred and dimmed, Ellie felt a great desire to call them back, to continue the sweet rejoicing with her siblings and resume that wonderful glow in her heart as she felt an expanding love for the Lord. For a moment, the pain and despair of the previous few weeks were all gone. But though she couldn't get her voice to work nor her hands to reach out for that circle of love, an overwhelming peace spread throughout her senses.

She began to see a faraway light that moved closer while glowing brighter.

Somehow, Ellie knew this light would bring a momentous change. It was a force of unmeasurable power, of unfathomable transformation from life as she had always known it to an ultra-vibrant being. Then she remembered Cay, Elsie, and Arvel. She yearned for this promise-filled light while feeling a strong reluctance to leave her dear husband and children — and the wonderful dream they shared.

Oh, what shall I do? Ellie asked in her heart, still fixated on the light but desiring the fruition of the dream of family for Cay and herself. As the increasing burden of weakness began to draw over her thoughts and spirit like a heavy black shroud, she faintly heard Cay's voice repeating, "We can make it!"

Oh yes, Cay! Yes, we can make it to our dream! Ellie tried to reply to her husband, yet she was vaguely aware the words had not risen vocally through the barrier of her weakness. *Oh Lord, have mercy on me! And on Cay! Please heal me and grant us our dream! Give us life and family, please, Lord, and I promise we'll live it for you!* Ellie's prayer burst forth from her agonizing heart while her pale lips remained silent, and she wondered if her prayer ever could be heard.

It was.

***

Billy and the group around him turned surprised faces toward the thundering hooves emitting from the dark road beyond the glow of the campfires and pine-knot torches in Shady Grove's yard. As curious revival attendees emerged sleepy-eyed from the nearby tents, a wagon careened around the last curve in the road with dirt and dust from wheels and hooves scattering in all directions. Billy instantly knew it was his brother-in-law Cay and that Ellie had to be extremely critical to warrant such a dangerous rate of speed.

Disheveled, unshaven, and obviously distraught, Cay

pulled hard against the leather reins, setting both bits firm into the open mouths of the foamed mule team before stomping down onto the long wooden brake handle. The wagon skidded sideways to a halt before the growing crowd.

"Billy! George!" he yelled hoarsely in a panic. "Everybody, please help us! Miss Ellie's in the back in a slow-fever coma! Please… do something!" Tears streaked down the desperate husband's dust-covered cheeks.

Striding swiftly toward the wagon, Billy motioned the others to close in as he stretched forth his hand and calmly said, "Give me a hand up there, Cay." George stepped up on the hub of the closest wagon wheel while Wille and Carl mounted into the wagon from the lowered rear gate. Others in the crowd, men and women alike, grouped as closely as possible and peered over the side rails at the tiny blanket-covered form.

Billy gazed lovingly into his sister's face as her closed eyelids flickered in short spasms, and his heart broke with the realization that unless the Good Lord intervened, Ellie was not long for this world. He looked up briefly and locked eyes first with George and then with Willie and Carl before turning to Cay, inches away and sideways on the wagon seat. The poor man stared at Billy with intensely imploring eyes.

"Cay, God tells us that where two or more are gathered together in His name, He is right there in the midst of them," Billy stated softly. "Our God gives us life, and He can and does save our life according to his goodwill and in accordance with our faith in him. I don't believe He gave y'all in marriage and brought your little children into this world to take Ellie home just yet. I believe God still has great purposes for her life here and that He is poised to work miracles of healing to fulfill His purposes in the days to come. When I got your telegram that my sister was deathly ill, I prayed hard for hours, during which time I perceived the Lord was telling me He had more plans for her and for me not to fear."

Cay let out a sigh of relief at these words.

"So, Cay, will you join with us all here as we pray now for Ellie's life, in full belief in the mercy and power of our God?"

Cay took a deep breath. A vivid memory suddenly flooded his conscience of Miss Ellie standing and smiling in the sunshine. This was the day she announced her pregnancy after they'd lost Lester the previous winter. He felt the hand of the Lord strong upon them as they prayed together that day, and an unexplainable reassurance swept over his spirit again under the trees of Shady Grove.

"Yes, I do believe in God's love and power over death and that He's with us right now, Billy." He continued in a more composed voice, "And Miss Ellie and I vowed together to trust Him and to put all our hope in Him, no matter what."

Billy grasped Cay's arm in affirmation of faith and brotherhood before turning to the others. With a humble but firm voice, he stated to all, "Let's reach out our hearts and our hands towards Ellie. Those close enough, place your hands upon her and let us all now pray, with faith, raising our voices unto the Good Lord for Ellie's healing."

Prayers rose from dozens of lips in unison, softly at first then gaining in crescendo as hearts moved in compassion for the couple. All had memories of loved ones lost to serious illness, and their souls hurt for Cay and Ellie as they longed for a repeat of the healing that some had witnessed during the revival. Their prayers carried a supernatural expectation due to these miracles. Their belief in the real power and compassion of God had been heightened from indisputable evidence, and the very atmosphere around the farm wagon seemed charged as the faithful prayers combined into one appeal for mercy. Though the words uttered were varied, they were unified and in one accord of the heart.

Carl felt this change and realized it had to be something beyond his comprehension, as no physical changes in climate or any other realm of earthly measure were evident. He felt his own prayers, so awkward in the beginning, becoming less of a human effort as he formulated words to a God he did not truly know. Carl's words begin to morph into an unconscious flow of love and compassion for the deliverance of Miss Ellie's life from the obvious clutches of death's dreadful hand.

He remembered his own mother and the terrible hurt her loss wrought on his heart. Carl revolted against another loss to the old adversary of death. His prayer became a weapon against it, as if his heart had taken on a separate life of its own. He felt rid of the dependence of his mind's habitual restrictiveness that formed throughout the years of harsh, disappointing realities and cruel-world experiences. The iron chains of doubt about the existence of God loosened and fell away as he prayed for Miss Ellie. A sense of freedom he had never before known welled up in his soul and was simultaneous with the assurance that Miss Ellie was absolutely being healed.

A short, quirky thought occurred to Carl that he was experiencing the blessed assurance of the song that had lured him to Shady Grove earlier. The voices he'd heard while deep in the woods sang again deep in his soul: "Blessed Assurance, Jesus is mine! Oh, what a foretaste of Heaven divine…"

With eyes tightly clenched, the prayers of intercession for Miss Ellie's healing turned into ever-increasing declarations of thanksgiving from Carl's smiling lips. Somehow, someway, he just knew Miss Ellie would be okay. With only slight shock, he realized his thanksgiving offering unto the Lord God was as much for his own deliverance from spiritual death as it was for Miss Ellie's physical deliverance. Carl felt as if the Lord's strong arms were wrapped around him, and he experienced a wonderful warmth as he had as a youngster when his sweet momma hugged him. It was the effects of natural, unselfish love upon his spirit, something he had missed without realizing it for all his adult years.

Another being's close presence was most definitely with him. Yes, God surely was real! Yes, Jesus did live and, just as the Bible said, gave up his earthly life upon that cross, taking the sins of mankind with him. Yes, Jesus did rise again to a life eternal and indestructible! Those previously doubtful readings in Alfonso's Bible came to authentic life. The truly good news of the Gospel now put rejoicing deep within him, where before there had, at best, been just wishful thinking when he read the scriptures.

That which was worldly and physically visible had been, for years, an imposing mountain obstructing the light of truth that was in Jesus Christ.

But God had just moved that mountain. Carl had an overpowering urge in his heart to share this wonderful awakening with others. And with it came another momentous change in his heart. A change he never thought possible. Carl now had the ability and also a surprising desire to truly forgive his kin who'd hurt and rejected him after his mother's death.

"Oh, Lord!" Carl whispered through quivering lips. "Please forgive me as I forgive my kinfolk! I'm so sorry for livin' like I have with hatred in my heart against 'em and for sinnin' against you. And I ask you to not hold nothin' against 'em, or me, please. As of right now, I release 'em completely for what they done, and I ask in your Holy Name, Lord Jesus, that you bless 'em both."

Pent-up tears from years of pain were loosed from his soul and streamed down both cheeks. For the first time in his entire life, he felt absolutely at peace and now really understood what Willie's daddy had explained to his son all those years ago.

Carl finally was, at last, a free man.

As he opened his eyes, now shining with great excitement, he beheld a miracle. He saw the beautiful sight of an obviously healthy Miss Ellie sitting fully upright in the wagon bed. She had a radiant smile upon her face, and both arms reached out to hug her trembling husband amid shouts of sheer joy from every voice in the churchyard at Shady Grove.

***

Carl Mitchell told Billy the next morning, "Preacher, I want you to know that I'll be a'comin to church regular from here on out 'cause I heard that huntin'-horn of God sound fer me at Miss Ellie's healing, just like Alfonso wrote about in my bible! I'm belongin' to the Good Lord now, and I ain't got any more doubts whatsoever."

Billy could see the evidence of change in Carl's eyes, and after both hugged one another, Billy said, "Old friend, what your heart heard was the powerful sound of God's trumpet, blown for the children of Israel to gather unto Him in Mount Sinai as we read in Exodus. And which will sound again someday when Christ returns for us all. Welcome to the family!"

A few weeks later, a letter arrived from Alfonso Steele in response to the news of Carl's conversion.

Dear Carl,

I write to you to share more about our fledging Texan Revolutionary Army as we retreated ahead of Santa Anna's forces after the Alamo fell.

General Sam Houston was undecided as to when and where we'd make a stand against such lopsided odds. Under 900 untrained frontiersmen (and many of them sick) were under his command at the time. Though Santa Anna had divided his forces, he still had 1500 or more men and another few thousand in Texas, mostly experienced, well-drilled, and well-equipped — a professional army.

Our men were spoiling for a fight. All were infuriated at the enemy's barbaric treatment of captured Texans at Goliad, who were told they'd be mercifully treated if they surrendered, but upon so doing were brutally executed.

Sam Houston knew we weren't ready for a pitched battle but heard the grumbling against retreating any further. On the road toward the U.S. border, Houston prayed for guidance to do what was right. Should we enter the U.S. and recruit more volunteers or find a good place to take a stand? At a fork in the road by the settlement of New Kentucky, our little army came abreast of a big live oak nicknamed "The Which Way Tree" by locals. One long limb pointed left towards the Sabine River and U.S. territory. The other pointed right, south to Harrisburg and the San Jacinto River, where Texican spies said Santa Anna would pass before turning north to intercept Houston's escape. Confident Houston would keep running that direction, Santa Anna arrogantly boasted he'd crush the last Texan resistance once and for all.

General Sam saw the limb, pointing right, as a sign from God and hollered, "We'll take the right way, boys!

The right road, and we'll take the fight to the enemy!"
We did so, and the rest is history. Santa Anna's forces
were soundly defeated in a battle lasting only 20
minutes.

You took the right way in your war, too, old friend. The
same God who delivered victory to us will do the same
for you. I'll say goodbye here and I will see you on the
other side of the river when next we meet. General Sam
and my compadres are all there now, and I'll introduce
you then.

~ A. Steele

Monument honoring the Battle of San Jacinto

Carl would be a faithful member of Shady Grove the rest
of his life, and his testimony led many others with hard
childhoods to Christ in the years to come.

Billy Harrison stayed in evangelism most of his life,
pastoring several churches in his elder years when constant

travel became physically prohibitive. George Harrison continued with his big brother on the evangelistic trail all through East Texas, eventually striking out on his own and expanding into parts of Louisiana. He became known for having committed the entire Bible to memory and for great workings of the Holy Spirit in his services for the next 70 years. The Azusa Street callings on both brothers made them pioneers of sorts, as they were among some of the earliest clergy in that region of Texas to insist on the integration of Blacks and all races into church congregations and camp meetings.

Both endured a few beatings, ostracism from some churches, and other hardships for several years over this decision, along with their professed belief in God's supernatural miracles. They even received an occasional death threat. Yet, they stayed true to the inclusive calling they'd received of God, including assisting Willie Davis in helping promote the church he founded after Miss Ellie's healing at Shady Grove.

Miss Ellie not only made a full and complete recovery, but was never sick another day in her nearly 90 years of living. Additionally, she found God restored her life and their dreams of family. He increased her as a midwife and prayer warrior, for her prayers over folks in the years to come usually resulted in quick recoveries. Some insisted she had the gift of the "laying on of hands," to which she always replied, "It's not me doing the healing, but our merciful God! All I do is have faith in Him!" When asked how one gets such a strong faith, Ellie explained, "If God healed you from certain death, in an instant as folks prayed like he did me, you'd have no problem with a lack of faith!"

Miss Ellie's daddy traded the bottle for a Bible after hearing of the miracle at Shady Grove. He led a sober and productive life thereafter.

Cay, who'd increased his daily Bible reading, relocated with Miss Ellie back to East Texas, where the drought was less severe and did not harm their crops. Their dreams of a flourishing farm and family bloomed in the ensuing years like the native evergreen magnolia trees, which blessed the senses every spring with dinner-plate-sized velvety white blooms and an alluring, sweet fragrance one could smell throughout the piney woods.

But there was more of life yet to unfold for Cay and Ellie's family and their descendants in the decades to come, for the Good Lord had wonderful plans for them all. For some, their faith would be tested in ways none could foretell.

Chapter Three: Saddlebaggers and War on Two Fronts

The spiraling wild muscadine wound more than 50 feet up the massive longleaf pine, the vine's loops so symmetrical as to appear like intricate carvings on wooden columns of some upscale southern mansion. In the late fall of 1918, at a season of the year when most muscadines had already dropped their lush fruits, this vine defied the norm and had goodly clumps of dark-purpled grapes. These natural delicacies dangled in a tantalizing display, growing in full view by the roadside just south of Shady Grove Church. A rustic split-rail fence zig-zagged directly in front of the big pine denoting Elton and Bertie Tucker's property line, making the whole scene all the more picturesque.

Miss Ellie Harrison Hughes spied the ripened muscadines as she rode past on her way to sweep out the church and help her brother George prepare for Wednesday evening's worship service.

My, but those would sure make a good batch of jelly! she thought to herself, and after a few moments, turned the buggy around to backtrack the quarter-mile to her sister Bertie's cabin. There today were all four of Ellie's kids, along with three of their seven cousins from Bertie and Elton Tucker's clan, playing in the sunshine on this lovely fall afternoon. This energetic bunch ranged from little four-year-old Vida Mae to 13-year-old Elsie and would surely pick a good mess of grapes before church started.

Miss Ellie's face burst into a wide smile as she watched

Vida Mae jump up and down with absolute delight upon receiving a tin pail and being told they were all going grape picking. Her lovely deep-blue eyes sparkled out from between bouncing light blond curly locks that seemed to be even more animated than the child's dancing legs.

"Ain't she just the cutest little cotton-topped pixie you ever saw!?!" declared Miss Ellie to Bertie, who was passing out empty tin pails to the others.

"She sure 'nuff is, Sis, and she's got a good head on her shoulders, too!" replied Bertie emphatically. Nodding in agreement, Miss Ellie thought back to when Vida Mae was just a toddler but had already started vocalizing several words and phrases far ahead of most her age. She was extra observant, frequently surprising Cay and Miss Ellie over the wide variety of objects around the farm she could find after briefly watching and listening to others in their daily duties. Both parents agreed she'd go far in this old world if given some education and opportunity.

Vida Mae's most notable trait was her sweet natural disposition towards everybody. This was evident even with the rough-housing boys of the family that sometimes picked at her in typical boyish crude ways, like passing gas at the dinner table, then pinching their noses while pointing mischievously at her. Little Vida Mae would just giggle along with everybody else instead of indignantly proclaiming her innocence as most children would do.

Other adults often remarked on her accelerated awareness along with her sweet personality. The church Sunday-school teacher told Ellie that when Vida Mae sang hymns such as 'Jesus Loves Me This I Know,' she seemed to have a spiritual intuition beyond her years. Hers seemed to be truly a song of worship to a God she understood as holy, rather than just a fun children's song that sounded catchy. She could be trusted to care for her little baby sister, Madeline, whom Vida

Mae could make smile at will with an assortment of silly sounds and facial contortions. She was treasured by all.

Watching and listening to their playful interactions brought many a whispered "Thank You, Lord!" from Miss Ellie's beaming face. She and Cay had thoroughly enjoyed the blessed life since she'd been healed of typhoid a decade before. After fetching Arvel and Elsie back from Floyd County to their new homestead near Woodville, Ellie had given birth to Matie in 1910, Vida Mae in 1914, and Madeline just last year in 1917. "And if the Good Lord wills it and the creek don't rise, we may not be through yet!" Miss Ellie would often declare. Cay agreed that as long as their health was good and the Lord kept putting food on the table, more children would suit him to a tee.

"Let's go, troops!" shouted 12-year-old Narlan Tucker, startling Miss Ellie's horse as she was mounting the buggy. Then he put the tin pail on top of his head, mimicking a soldier's helmet while commanding the others with a hearty, "Follow me!" before bursting into a rousing rendition of the popular wartime song "Over There." As Miss Ellie gained control of the jumpy young Palomino stallion, she was amused at Narlan's antics as he led his excited bunch in a quasi-military assault toward the passive muscadine vine. Then she was instantly sobered, for this charade reminded her that America was in the throes of a devastating World War. World War One seemed distant in one respect since the battlefields were an ocean away, yet perilously close to home in another. Many of their close neighbors and relatives were drafted or had joined the military. They were fighting for their lives while the folks back home picked grapes and sang hymns in church.

George and Ellie's younger brother, Jerry Harrison, had embarked a year ago for basic training in the U.S. Army and was now overseas in France with the American

Expeditionary Force. Remembering George had planned a special prayer service that evening for all the troops, Miss Ellie popped the reins on the stallion's rump to hasten on to church. She waved goodbye to the happily marching children as horse and buggy turned north through the cedar rail gate onto the main road.

Within moments, Miss Ellie rode past the soon-to-be plucked muscadine vine and its host tree. She casually glanced in that direction while wishing she could join the kids for what promised to be an enjoyable and profitable time of gathering. A sudden chill of foreboding flitted across her senses. Quick as it had come, the sense of impending danger struck and then was gone. Miss Ellie slowed the horse and scanned the area more carefully for any obvious reason why this premonition of dread could have been triggered, but her sweeping gaze revealed nothing evident. After a few moments of indecision of whether to turn the buggy around and intercept the kids or continue on to the church, she chose the latter. Maybe the earlier thoughts of war had transposed tragedy upon her subconsciousness to interrupt this peaceful day, Ellie reasoned. But without any real signs of trouble, Ellie deemed it foolish to stop the kids from their goal, and therefore she proceeded to hurry on to Shady Grove.

It was a choice she would later regret.

***

Swinging the heavy brass belt buckle in a wide downward arc, Cane Bass snapped his muscular wrist at the last moment to create a bullwhip-like motion in the leather belt for added impact as the strike landed behind George Harrison's left knee. The blow brought a sharp cry from George as he toppled sideways onto the dirt road. He'd just assumed a stooped position to pick up the hymn books spilled from his saddlebags that Cane had jerked off George's horse. This happened only moments after Kent Bass, sometimes called "Jug" (so named for his illegal whiskey still business), dumped George off his mount with a violent shove from a leathery, dirt-stained hand.

The burly pair had surprised George, stepping quickly out of the woods two miles before Shady Grove Church. George was slow-walking his horse that direction to preach an evening service. The ensuing attack was swift and obviously preplanned.

"When are you pansy-faced, holy-roller, saddlebaggers gonna learn?!" Cane asked with a sneer through his matted reddish beard.

"Yeah, we done told ya once not to show yer skinny tail in these parts no more!" Jug added through clenched teeth. "Cause if ya do, we'll yank you outta that meetin' house and beat you to within an inch of yer life! We've had a belly full of yer kind stirrin' up the womenfolk with that Holy Joe talk and cuttin' into our business, preachin' that corn liquor oils the gates of Hell!" He concluded by spitting a dark brown stream of chewing tobacco onto George's trouser leg.

"Now, you git on that nag an keep on a ridin' through Shady Grove's yard, an don't ya stop 'til yer clear outta this here county!" Cane threw over his shoulder as the stocky figures stepped back towards the thick woods from which they'd come.

"Sure wish you boys would get another hobby," George muttered while rubbing his throbbing knee as his antagonists melted back into the brush with the stealth of born backwoodsmen. "As roughing up a lone preacher half your size is liable to smear your upstanding reputation in the community!" he added louder, feeling that this parting sarcasm was at least a small rebuke for the injustice suffered.

A sharp, rough "Git!" rang back from the brushy woodline, motivating George to hasten a mite quicker in dusting off his hymn books and repacking them into the bulky saddlebags.

Both brothers reeked of corn liquor, which George surmised could've been either from recent consumption or ingrained in their trademark tattered denim overalls, as neither's garments nor their hairy hides showed any encounters with soap for a month of Sundays. Yet he knew to take their threats seriously, as the pair had attacked his brother Billy a few years earlier, harshly beating him and even cutting the tail off his mule. A few others in the area opposed Pentecostal preachers and other non-mainstream beliefs, but most of their opposition was just verbal.

However, a select few resorted to violence, and the Bass brothers were among the worse. George knew they meant business, and it was just one more of many concerns that plagued him lately.

The life of itinerant evangelists — or saddlebaggers, so named for carrying extra saddlebags of Bibles and hymnals — required travel to various locations for regular church services. These roaming preachers often substituted for a local pastor (as George was now at Shady Grove) or held weeks-long revivals. It was wearying and challenging work. For some reason lately, perhaps due to the wartime economy, the church offerings that sustained George had been very slim.

He was down to just a few dollars pocket change. When there were no invites to supper from local church folks, he sometimes subsisted on one meager meal a day. Each week George sent money home to his young wife, Clara, to sustain their two small children 80 miles away. He sent all he had during extra lean times, trusting the Lord to provide for his own needs on the road. George hadn't seen his little family in six weeks, and he missed them terribly.

George often felt like he and his family were fighting multiple wars, and the battle fatigue was getting him down. The Bass brothers represented the ancient yet contemporary war on Christianity, where such shadowy figures seemed always fixated on destroying those called to God's ministry. It amazed George that some people could get so worked up over a Gospel message that represented a lasting peace, encouraged goodwill to all, and threatened no physical bodily harm. It did involve a truthful warning that a personal free choice to live sinfully would result in extreme danger of eternal punishment from a fair God. Just as anybody would warn a traveler of a faulty bridge over a treacherous canyon to avert certain death by avoiding that course of travel, true Christians of any denomination preached that belief in Jesus Christ and the resultant moral changes were needed to save the eternal soul.

George only wanted folks to know of this good news of salvation, but some took it as a personal assault and wanted to respond in kind. The constant physical danger was real, and though the cause was worth it in the end and George would never back off from his calling, the strain eventually took a toll on his energy, sleep patterns, and spiritual focus.

It wasn't lost on George that those who opposed him whole hog were those who somehow thought he represented a threat to their income or prestige, rather than those who differed with his Pentecostal message. To the latter, where the act of speaking in tongues brought frowning faces and a charge of "misleading" folks as to requirements of being saved, George could usually reason with them. He calmly explained that this was an element of the baptism of the Holy Spirit and that one can indeed be saved through the belief and surrender unto Christ's deity with an assurance of Heaven, never having spoken in tongues. He also explained that ever since his experience at Azusa Street (and years after that) of personal encounters with the power of the Holy Spirit, he sometimes spoke in tongues which richly enhanced his personal relationship with the Good Lord. This usually cleared up some misconceptions about his Pentecostal faith.

Yet it was not so much a physical fear, the loss of old friendships or finances, nor hostile misunderstandings that put a shudder in his thin frame, for he had the courage born not of transient idealism but a sure calling from God Almighty. Justifiable wars, both physical and spiritual, needed to be fought. George did fear, however, that because of weariness, he might let his Savior down. He worried that his purpose and effectiveness as a minister for the Lord had of late suffered to some degree.

Failures are an inevitable part of living. But failing Christ was unacceptable. That's what scared him.

Then there was an actual World War with horrific and extensive loss of life through this terrible conflict. And as if that weren't bad enough, the war was joined this year by another monstrous killer via the Spanish Influenza pandemic. World War I accounted for millions already killed in Europe, but this awful invisible death struck Americans by the thousands at home. For the Harrisons and their neighbors, this was extra catastrophic, as several young men they knew had been in Army camps known to have had flu outbreaks.

George and Ellie's little brother, Jerry, was now fighting overseas in France, and the family hadn't received any news of him for over a month. In his last letter, Jerry recounted a story he'd heard of some American troops that were killed instantly by the new high explosive artillery shells. These detonations supposedly sucked the breath from their lungs by the terrific percussion of the shell bursts.

According to the rumor, the dead were discovered

without any external wounds. All were found still standing or crouching as they'd been before the barrage, frozen in place with uniforms unruffled and helmets on heads, staring lifelessly into nothing like macabre statues. The worry within George over his little brother's life, as threatened by both a high-explosive war and insidious disease, was constant.

The intense war had embroiled George on two fronts, and just like any soldier, he sometimes needed off the front lines for a spell. He pondered that even the Old Testament Prophet, Elijah, had required a period of rest and food after contesting with the people about their worship of false gods. Subsequent death threats from Queen Jezebel had belabored him to the point of asking God just to end his life in the wilderness. An angel from God fed Elijah and caused him to sleep, saying, "…the journey is too great for thee." In this manner, the Lord provided what Elijah needed for the days to come. So also was rest and nourishment needed for George. And sister Ellie could be his angel for this purpose.

George, therefore, thought of stopping by Cay and Ellie's farm for a week or two for "refreshing" and quiet personal time spent with the Lord in prayer while meditating on the Word. Both George and Billy had done so at various times while on the evangelist's trail through the years. Their momma had died young, leaving four single boys, of which two were in their teens, to face life under the harsh authority of an alcoholic father. Ellie and Cay's house had been their home away from home, as she loved her little brothers with her whole heart, considering their well-being to be her responsibility. The couple kindly required nothing in return. Ellie would cook their meals, mend and wash their clothes, while Cay looked after and fed their mules. As they matured and became family men in later years, the brother's wives and kids would join them at Ellie's for a few days to sweeten the experience.

Yes, George decided he'd mention this to Ellie when he got to Shady Grove Church this afternoon. With her approval, as soon as the home preacher recovered from his bout with the Spanish flu, George would park the seat of his saddle-worn britches on the front porch at the Hughes family farm. But it could take weeks to recover from the dreaded flu, especially when the stricken preacher told folks his fever was so high that he feared his eyebrows would catch fire. Still, the thought of visiting the Hughes family was balm to his aching knee and sagging spirits, eliciting a "gitty-up!" from rider to horse as George looked forward to seeing his sister. She was always immensely helpful to her family and friends, and her cheerful devotion to the Lord encouraged one to forget their sorrows and embrace the gift of life. George prayed for Ellie and her family all the way to Shady Grove's yard.

***

Scrambling through and over the split rail fence, the children dispersed around the muscadine-wrapped tree at various positions assigned by young Narlan Tucker. Little Vida Mae was to start at the right base of the trunk to gather the grapes closest to ground level as befitting her stature and experience, with a warning to watch for briars and snakes. This caused immediate widening of those pretty blue eyes as she stepped sharply backward in her oversized big brother's hand-me-down leather hunting boots. Her spooked reaction sparked a chuckle from Narlan, who was already climbing up an elm tree just behind the tomboyish Matie. The elm had two forks at various levels that lapped close to the big pine and had some branched sprouts of the fruit-laden muscadine vine within easy reach. Narlan hollered down to Elsie Hughes and his brothers, Osh and Joe, to move back a bit from the spot where they were picking grapes. He didn't want them directly underneath in case he or Matie dropped their tin pail.

Within the half-hour, most of the kids had pails at least half full of ripe muscadine grapes. As Narlan began to climb down to examine the ground around the tree for dropped grapes, he glanced up to tell Matie to follow in descent. Matie was climbing higher with one hand while holding her nearly full pail in the other.

"Matie!" he yelled, "What in the world do you think you're doing?!"

"There's some big muscadines at the top of this fork!" Matie hollered back without turning her head. "When I get 'em, I'll come down with more grapes than you, and I'll win that bet we got into with Uncle Elton!" she added, stepping high out onto a slim elm branch.

Narlan glanced down at the others who were shading their eyes against the afternoon sun and peering upward to watch Matie's perilous ascent. All except Vida Mae, who spilled some of her booty when squeezing under the bottom rails of the fence. She scrambled to pick up the scattered grapes.

"Y'all help Vida Mae! And get her back by the road until Matie uses what little sense she was born with and comes down out of that dumb tree!" Narlan exclaimed, frustrated at Matie's daredevil climb and the fact she'd probably beat him and win the bet. The prize was a ride in a motorized truck tomorrow with a well-to-do neighbor who'd be picking up Elton Tucker for a trip to town.

Just as Narlan turned his head back after watching the others clear the fence, he heard a loud splintering noise followed instantly by a resounding scream. The upper elm branch snapped off under Matie's weight, sending her tumbling downward. Spinning like a flipped coin head over heels, she fell 20 feet. Narrowly missing Narlan, Matie landed flat on the small of her back onto the top wooden rail of the fence.

The little group heard a sharp "crack" upon the impossibly hard impact as Matie's body bent almost double backward before recoiling off the rail. As all watched in shocked disbelief, her limp form crumpled like a paper doll onto the sandy ground outside the fence. She'd struck the fence in the exact spot where little Vida Mae had been seconds earlier.

Narlan sprung quickly down to crouch next to an unresponsive Matie. As expected from such a horrific fall, Matie showed no signs of life. No rising and falling of the chest in drawing breath. No flicker of the eyes or twitches of the eyelids. No expression of pain upon Matie's strangely peaceful and pale features. One might think she was only sleeping, except for the left arm bent awkwardly under her torso and her chin tucked uncomfortably far down into her chest. Her signature dark chestnut brown ponytail flopped forward over one freckled cheek.

Young Narlan Tucker's usually nimble mind seemed paralyzed, unable and unwilling to perceive what the stark evidence was declaring to him: that death had just stolen Matie away. All the children stood in numbed silence. Only the subdued sounds of a gentle north breeze rustling nearby leaves were heard, and an unseen cardinal was tweeting a merry tune, as if all of nature was stoically unmoved by the harshest of human tragedies displayed under a cloudless blue sky.

"Quick, let's pray together!" one of the kids exclaimed (none could recall later who'd said this, and each, when questioned individually, denied it). All in the group dropped to their knees around Matie, set the tin pails on the ground, joined hands, and began to pray. Theirs was the unrehearsed, simple prayers of kids, devoid of any hint of sophistication or awareness of how well-phrased their words sounded. Most were crying and sobbing as they pleaded with their whole hearts for Matie's life. Within a short time, Narlan wiped his tear-streaked cheeks and, seeing a small movement out of the corner of his eye, glanced sideways at Matie's face and saw her lips part slightly to draw in a breath of air.

"Joe! Run get Momma and Papa real fast! And tell 'em to bring the wagon right away!" Narlan cried out. Joe, still praying loudly, sprang swiftly to his feet, knocking over his pail of muscadines, and was ten feet down the road before Narlan had finished his last sentence. The others continued to pour out their prayers as Joe sprinted nimbly away, with his arms pumping wildly and small spurts of sand flung backward from his heels with each lunging stride.

Vida Mae scooted on her knees closer to Matie and laid her tiny hand upon her sister's shoulder, then looked sweetly up at Narlan. He heard her soft voice saying, "Don't cry, Narlan. I asked Lord Jesus to please tell Matie's life to come back home. He said He will."

Fifteen minutes later, Matie raised her head and looked around in bewilderment at her family, still as statues and staring down at her. She began to realize with a slow-dawning curiosity that she was lying on Uncle Elton's wide front porch. Uncle Elton had an intensely troubled expression and was crouched next to her along with Aunt Bertie. Someone had put a wet rag on her throbbing forehead, and Aunt Bertie reached forward with tender concern to remove it, asking, "Matie dear, how do you feel?"

Matie could only stare numbly back, disoriented and struggling with her re-emerging conscience to figure out what was wrong.

After a long pause, Uncle Elton said, "Matie, just stay still for a bit. Can you feel your back?"

Then it all came rushing back to Matie about picking

muscadines and climbing higher than Narlan and the bet as to who could pick the most. At that thought, Matie looked quickly around the porch to her left and right. She seemed to be searching for something. Aunt Bertie leaned closer again to get Matie's attention and once more questioned, "Oh, Matie! Can't you talk? Please say something, dear!"

Matie brought her now-focused eyes to meet those of Aunt Bertie's, and to the absolute astonishment of all, said with a clear and healthy voice, "Where are my muscadines?"

Ellie's horse and buggy were two strides behind George, who had Joe Tucker sitting behind him. They raced both horses into the Tucker's yard, expecting to find anything but the loud peals of laughter ringing forth from the big porch. Bertie rushed over to them as they reigned to a halt and hurriedly explained that Matie seemed to be fine except for some bruising on her back. Ten minutes earlier, a breathless and tearful Joe had told both Ellie and George at Shady Grove's yard about Matie's fall and that she "looked like a goner!" They'd quickly mounted in a panic and hit the road at a dead run with almost-incoherent prayers, slowing only when abreast of the muscadine vine. Joe pointed out where the elm branch had broken and the place upon the rail fence where Matie's body impacted.

With a horrified expression, George exclaimed simply, "Lordy, Lordy!" at the extremes of young Matie's fall. Ellie began pleading to God, "Oh, mercy! Lord have mercy on her!" before both raced off again.

An incredulous Elton Tucker was still gingerly touching Matie's lower back and asking endless questions about her pain levels when Ellie and George rushed onto the porch. As Ellie cupped Matie's face in her hands, Elton explained what had happened before they'd arrived and concluded with, "By all rights, this child should be either dead or seriously crippled. All I can figure is that the Lord's hand cushioned her fall!"

Typical split rail fence found on woodland properties.

Matie, who had already sat up straight, stood up and raised the back of her shirt to let her mother and Uncle George see for themselves how little bruising was showing there. The other kids were still laughing uproariously at Matie's untimely concern over muscadines while excitedly recounting how scared they'd been. They were amazed at God's obvious deliverance of her life. Narlan kept repeating, "She wasn't even breathing! Not at all!"

Only little Vida Mae seemed unsurprised and sat calmly on the top step, smiling at Matie. Narlan walked over to Ellie and George and told them of Vida Mae's assurance that Jesus said He'd tell Matie's life to come back. Later, they took Vida Mae aside, and after a few minutes, George asked, "Did Jesus really tell you he'd save your sister's life — you heard his voice speaking?"

"Yes, sir," Vida Mae answered. "I prayed and asked him

to, 'cause I remembered when my kitty cat's life went away and how sad I was. I told Jesus if Matie's life went away, I'd be sad forever, and Momma would be, too. I asked Jesus to please not let that happen."

"Uncle George," she continued, "you tell us to believe Jesus." Her big blue eyes shined with honest transparency. "So, I did."

As George rode out of the Tucker's yard, he pondered how the faith of a small child could do so much for the encouragement and resurgence of faith within a grown man. And in this case, a man exposed to miracles before and who had been called by God to preach. His previous fears of failure and extreme weariness were gone. As he passed the muscadine vine with its rounded, heart-shaped leaves, George decided to dismount to say a prayer of thanksgiving. Kneeling by that split rail fence, George felt the presence of the Holy Spirit so strong as to rival some of his experiences at Azusa Street. He remembered his brother Billy's telegram to Cay when Ellie was facing death and the line stating that "life is here" at Shady Grove. He knew that this gift of life could happen anywhere, anytime, when plain folks—even if they're only kids — trust the Good Lord and pray in faith according to His Word.

George felt so inspired by the Spirit of God while praying that instead of just a scheduled Church service set to begin in a few hours, he hoped a revival would start to pour out tonight. At the very least, George concluded, it will be a time of great rejoicing tonight over a child's life saved this day. As he stood up, he saw Narlan approaching with a pail in hand. "What're you doing back here, Narlan?" he inquired.

"I told Matie she'd won the bet.," Narlan replied. "And that her muscadines spilled, so I offered to come back and get them for her. Wished I'd taken a drink first, though, as I'm real thirsty, but I was in a hurry to make Matie happy."

"Climb over the fence here to this muscadine vine, Narlan, and I'll show you how the Good Lord provides," George said while swinging his long legs over the top rail. George pulled out his Barlow pocketknife, stooped over at the base of the big pine, and cut through a section of the attached muscadine vine. Pulling the vine above the cut loose from the tree, he handed the cut end to an inquisitive Narlan.

Narlan could see a few tiny drops of moisture beginning to seep out of the cut.

"You want me to drink this little bit of sap, Uncle George?" he inquired.

"Hold your horses, Narlan, oh ye of little faith!" George answered with a twinkle in his eye. "Don't tell me a country boy like you, and a Christian child to boot, doesn't know how the Lord created a way for us to live when he made these woods?" George added.

Narlan looked more confused.

"Looky here; you reach up with your knife hand, real high kinda like you're gonna reach up to Heaven in a praise to God for his bounty. Then you take that knife — think of it as the sword of the Spirit — and you cut that old vine all the way through and drink from the blessings of the Lord!" George stated as he sliced through the vine a second time about seven feet up from the first cut while still holding the upper portion of the severed vine upright. The few drips began to increase from the lower cut until a small but steady ribbon of sweet, nourishing liquid seeped into Narlan's opened mouth. After a few moments, Narlan's thirst was mostly quenched, and he looked up at a smiling George.

"Thanks, Uncle George! That tastes real good!" he exclaimed.

George gave him a quick hug and said, "You're mighty welcome, nephew. See you at church tonight, where you'll get a better nectar than muscadine water!" He waved as he mounted his horse and began to hum praise songs on the road to Shady Grove.

George Harrison, the revived revivalist, was ready and bursting with the desire to share the good news of Christ's Gospel again. But neither George nor Narlan knew that one day in another future world war, this shared teaching about the muscadine vine would save the life of Narlan's little brother, Osh, as he was stranded and hiding from the Japanese Army in the jungles of a remote Pacific island.

***

While shaking hands and greeting folks on the front steps at Shady Grove, George heard the sweet sound of children's voices singing and shouting before the Tucker family's big wagon appeared around the last bend of the road. Pulling into the churchyard, the youngsters scrambled off the wagon far ahead of Elton, Bertie, Cay, and Ellie, several feet before the rig came to a complete halt.

"What's the big hurry, kids?" George quipped as the children ran forward to give him multiple hugs. "Y'all scared old Slewfoot will get you before you get inside?" he continued with a wide smile.

"No, Uncle George, we're just happy for how God kept Matie from getting bad hurt," Elsie Hughes said with flushed cheeks while emitting a strong vapor of her mother's lilac perfume. "And we just know that God is waiting for us inside Shady Grove, so we can't wait to be in there with Him," she gushed with girlish excitement. This last statement greatly touched George's heart, and he gave her another hug while looking up into the sweet expressions on Ellie and Bertie's faces. Both communicated to him their matching joy in sharing their kids' love of the Lord's house.

George felt an extra awareness of the presence of God that had escalated in the past two hours since Matie's stunning recovery and the big faith of little Vida Mae.

George felt in his bones that the Good Lord was working on something special tonight to punctuate the grace and mercy already enacted this beautiful evening. He'd been led while praying before the service to read in the book of Romans. Some scriptures leaped out at him, and they emphasized how the power of the Spirit springs forth from the Word of God and imbues a special faith to mankind. These scriptures reinforced in George what he'd learned the last few years — that the dedicated reading of one's Bible along with a prayer for understanding was the key that unlocked the door to a higher faith. And this big faith often manifests itself in the unlikeliest of people. Faith is the surest producer of real hope, a hope so strong as to carry one through the deadliest of life's storms when all may seem lost. The power of real hope within a person suppresses the paralyzing fears and doubts a violent storm imposes.

Spinning off from this hope is the highly treasured gift of peace, as Jesus describes the Holy Spirit as a Comforter for the child of God. George's understanding was ultra-focused on this precept after the day's wide cycle of events, as earlier in the day, his peace of mind was a frayed and flimsy garment. The Good Lord changed all that. George greatly appreciated God's gift of comforting peace as a vital part of the believer's inheritance. It's a special kind of peace of the Spirit that cannot be disavowed, stolen, or bullied away, nor destroyed by war or pandemics.

All of George's doubts about failing his Lord, his fears for his family, his dread of both types of wars, and his physical protection drifted away like the smoke from a snuffed-out fire.

One scripture he read just before people started arriving

for church seemed to demand his attention. George wasn't entirely sure what to make of it. In Romans Chapter 16 and verse 20, George read, "And the God of peace shall bruise Satan under your feet shortly." George was a bit puzzled, as he felt the God of peace had already worked a miraculous defeat of death today, which Satan represents in many ways. Also, in doing it, God had affected the faith of all the members of Matie's family and would encourage countless more as the story of her deliverance spread.

What else was there left to do in the here and now? George puzzled.

By 7 p.m., people were coming in and being seated as George, who never made written notes but memorized the gist of his message while relying on the Holy Spirit, stepped up to the podium to open services with a prayer. Upon raising his head at the conclusion of prayer, George was pleasantly surprised to see the church house was almost full — unusual for a Wednesday service. Like adding fuel to a fire, this stoked the flame of the Gospel in George, which became evident as he led the congregation in several worship songs with a bold and extra-rich baritone voice. With great gusto, he began to preach about the power of faith that overcomes evil and death by starting with the life of the prophet Elijah from the book of Kings.

George recounted the death of a child in 1 Kings 17:17 where "...there was no breath left in him." Then with his voice rising, he referred to verse 21, where Elijah prayed and cried unto the Lord, "...let this child's soul come into him again." George turned his shining blue eyes, alight with the fire of a heart filled with a love of sharing the truth of God's mercy and power, toward the pew where the muscadine kids sat in wide-eyed silence.

"There sits pretty Matie Hughes, my friends, where a few hours ago was thought to have been given over to the clutched hand of death after a fall from a height to match this church's roofline!" George declared with his right hand leveled at a blushing Matie. "But for the prayers of these young children, one of which is only four years old," George swept his eyes all around the crowd for emphasis before continuing with a widening spread of his arms, "in absolute faith in the merciful power of our Lord, she who had no breath before having her soul returned is now here to rejoice with us tonight! Can I get somebody here to join me in giving thanks to the Almighty for Matie and the faith of these children!?!"

As the congregants shouted "Amen," George looked heavenward with upright hands. "Oh, but I feel the power of the Lord putting a mighty strong preach in me tonight, and it's itching to bust loose!"

Everyone leaped to their feet with resounding applause while looking towards Matie, and some were shouting "Praise God!" or "Hallelujah!" for theirs was a close community, and most knew and loved the Tucker and Hughes families. Matie's miracle was extra poignant to the group, for a child's life was most precious to the folks of Shady Grove, where many families had through the rigors of farm life buried a child or two over the years. It was indeed an occasion for great rejoicing that the gate to the nearby graveyard would remain firmly latched, and the hope for endless contributions from a young life still stretched forth brightly into the pathways of the future.

Amid the great celebration and as all eyes were directed towards Matie, Elton nudged Bertie and discreetly nodded to the entrance doors behind them. Bertie immediately recognized the two young couples who'd quietly slipped inside and edged slowly to the empty pew directly behind Ellie and Cay. The girls were sisters in their late teens, whose parents were very wealthy as measured by country folks' standards. Both had been here once before, and Bertie remembered they came to mock and poke fun at the "Holy-Rollers," for neither attended any church. Like many of their ilk, they were looking for unique ways to ease their perpetual boredom. Bertie only knew them by their nicknames, "Feathers" and "Spunky", but she couldn't recall the names of their escorts.

3-year-old Vida Mae (top left) with siblings Arvel, Matie, and Elsie holding baby Madelene. 1917.

As Bertie tried to get Ellie's attention, she saw one of the young men had a pint liquor bottle showing slightly from a coat pocket. She silently prayed they were not too drunk and that they would not disrupt the service.

George was indeed being led by the Holy Spirit, as his preaching was liberally mixed with fervent praises flowing steadily outward from a man ordained by God and who was freshly inspired by the great faith of small children. The Lord's presence was becoming evident throughout Shady Grove. Men, women, boys, and girls were all riveted on the message of the power to overcome any challenge through faith. George's preaching transcended far beyond just spoken words; imparting into the souls of all there a fuller reality of what was — at least to the unsaved world — an abstract quality, yet to believers was a spiritually profound power derived from a saving faith in Jesus Christ. His building enthusiasm was captivating, as George was physically caught up in the moment, displaying increased gestures and movements around the podium. George preached God's Word with a heightened fervor, obviously directed by the palpable presence of the Holy Spirit.

Twenty minutes into the service, the two unbelieving couples who Ellie earlier heard make sarcastic jokes were no longer mocking and chuckling. Their expectations for entertainment had morphed into a more serious event. They, too, could sense something out of the ordinary was developing before their eyes.

The witnessing of a faith that transforms and heals both the visible and invisible distresses of human existence began to ring a chord in their inner being.

The words of scripture from the tenth chapter of Romans, George's favorite, began to be prayed and repeated as he lifted his face and hands, and his voice took on a different tone. George's thin frame started to slightly tremble as he half-sang and half-spoke, "The word is within thee, even in thy mouth, and in thine heart; that is the word of faith…". Then he repeated it louder with a vibrato in his voice that did not sound like him, and his eyes were raised and fixed intently upward.

Abruptly the entrance doors burst open at that point, and in stomped a furious Cane and Kent Bass, startling the entire congregation. Everyone spun around in their seats toward the intruders as Cane bellowed, "What'd we tell you, saddle bagger!?! Now yur gonna get what's comin' to ya!" Before anyone could react, both red-faced brothers stormed up the center aisle and jumped up onto the platform. George had not moved a muscle nor looked away, still powerfully focused upward with opened hands raised high in praise.

Reaching up and forward, Kent grabbed George by his right forearm, and Cane did the same on George's left. As the brothers' rough hands grasped his thin arms tightly, both braced their stout legs wide and yanked hard towards the steps, intent on dragging George Harrison down the center aisle and out of the Lord's house.

Cay and Elton rose to take a step towards the aisle, desiring to intervene for George as they recognized the seriousness of the threat. Both Cane and Kent Bass looked angry enough to kill.

That's when the impossible happened. Again.

To the astonishment of everyone — especially the Bass brothers —neither one of them could budge George. He stood like a solid granite statue with all his being focused on praising God, not moving so much as a fraction of an inch from his position. The brothers glanced into each other's startled eyes briefly before drawing in a big breath and exerted all their strength in another terrific pull on George's arms. This time, though George's body still didn't move at all, both his hands pivoted around from the wrists and downward, clamping hard upon the muscular forearms of Cane and Kent Bass with a dreadful pressure that felt more akin to a mechanical device than a human hand.

Now the bewildered and extremely agitated brothers began in earnest to pull and tug wildly with all their might in various directions to free themselves in any way they could. But the iron vice of the skinny preacher's hands continued to hold fast. To make the whole scene even more incredulous to the goggle-eyed audience watching, George was still praying and praising as if nothing had changed. Nothing in his demeanor suggested even slightly that there was anyone next to him, much less two ferocious whiskey-breathed galoots that collectively outweighed him by over 300 pounds.

Every fiber of his body and soul was wholly focused on his Creator and Lord.

After a few moments of useless struggle, and with their crushed arms going numb, both panicked Bass brothers frantically begged and pleaded for George to release them. Gone was their harsh demeanor, and gone forever was their perception that they would bully any more clergy. Though he still did not acknowledge their existence in the least, George's bony hands relaxed their grip and resumed their upward praise.

The abruptly freed brothers fell awkwardly and painfully backward off the three-foot-high platform to land in a pathetic heap on the oaken floor at George's feet. Both scrambled upright, looking wide-eyed as they ran, stumbling for the exit doors. Bursting outside, Cane and Kent dashed madly down the dirt road until out of sight of the dumbfounded congregation.

To all onlookers, it appeared as if the proverbial hounds of Hell were snapping at their backsides.

Still oblivious of what had transpired, George Harrison

could later only shake his head in wonder when told of the one-sided struggle. He began to understand what the Lord had foretold him in the Roman verses prior to the service. When some in the congregation asked George how in the world he stood so firm against such a force, he said he didn't know. He only knew it wasn't from his own power or any source in this world.

The simple conclusion was that God takes care of his own, and not even Satan or his minions, however powerful they may seem, can thwart the purposes of God or stop his Word from being served up to his children. The Lord had indeed bruised Satan and laid him at the feet of His chosen minister. George was never physically accosted again once the story of that incredible night circulated among believing and disbelieving alike. His ministry calling was made ironclad within his heart.

He would get wearied again in the future but never again fearful.

A revival did start that night at Shady Grove. The next night, the two previously disbelieving and mocking sisters walked humbly down the same aisle where they had stepped in jaunty ridicule of God's reverence the day before. Answering the altar call, they surrendered their hearts to the lordship of Jesus Christ. Both girls became ministers in their own right, and served the Lord well all their lives.

Many others followed suit as the reality of the Kingdom of God spread throughout Tyler County. The revival carried forward for weeks, finally ending on November 11, 1918. This was also the day that World War I, known as "The War to End All Wars," officially ended.

George's wife, Clara, sent him a letter right after Thanksgiving, detailing how she hadn't wanted to tell him she'd run out of money that week and how she and the kids planned on having only rice for Thanksgiving supper. As they were praying at the table and giving thanks for the rice, a neighbor knocked on their door to offer an elaborate five-course meal, saying some planned company had disappointed them and left them with more food than they could eat.

George's teardrops peppered the letter, and he left early the next morning to rejoin his family. Their rejoicing could be heard five houses down the street upon his arrival.

George's brother Jerry Harrison survived the war unhurt and arrived back in Texas just before Christmas. It was a Christmas to remember, for both victorious warriors had returned home.

"Uncle" Jerry Harrison, 2nd from right on the top ledge with fellow soldiers in his unit, taken in France at the close of WWI".

The Bass brothers' fierce reputation against God's ministers was forever diminished once the account of their inglorious retreat from a skinny preacher spread throughout Tyler County. Folks began to jokingly refer to Cane and Kent as "Came and Went."

Though George prayed for their souls, neither brother was ever seen again near Shady Grove.

***

American agricultural products took a nosedive in the post-war years as European farmers started producing again. Supply outweighed demand through the 1920s and into the 1930s. Contrarily, oil and gas industries exploded as the economic need for fuel from an expanding mechanized world created opportunities galore in Texas, at least for a while. Cotton had been dethroned, and oil was now the undisputed king. Farm plows were left idle in the fields as petroleum raised the promise of prosperity, along with cities that beckoned one and all to join the parade into a modern tomorrow.

Cay and Ellie sold their farm one spring and moved south near the burgeoning cities of Port Arthur and Port Neches along the Gulf Coast. With their Model T Ford truck packed to capacity, they took one final farewell glance at their farm. Before joining the southern human migration from the Texas farming interior to the big city refineries, they raised a prayer skyward for safe travel. There Cay spotted the wild geese continuing their usual northern migration for the season, and a wry smile of appreciation came upon his upturned face. He almost envied their slow, steady wing beats that seemingly oozed confidence that better days would lie ahead in the Good Lord's bounty beyond the northern skyline.

They were going one direction because of certain old instincts, and he was heading the opposite in an uncertain hope of a new future. Cay recollected the red-tailed hawk from years ago and thought of how God had taught him the value of trusting in His lordship before saving Miss Ellie's life during that desperate journey. With that encouraging memory boosting his confidence, Cay thanked God ahead of time for this new phase of life and dismissed any doubts for the future.

Many of the Harrison clan moved to work in refineries, and the ensuing dozen years proved fruitful. Families grew and prospered, and the Lord's churches along the coastal cities expanded with them into the new era, building parking lots for clusters of motorized vehicles where hitching rails for horse and buggy once stood.

Vida Mae Hughes graduated valedictorian of her high school class of 1931. She'd sewed her own graduation dress, for the recent economic collapse known as "The Great Depression" had of necessity resurrected the pioneer art of self-sufficiency. Cay still worked his refinery job, albeit for a hard cut in pay and greatly reduced hours. But he praised God that he could still buy the needed staple goods and pay the mortgage on their small home while raising a thriving vegetable garden. He usually had plenty and gave to hungry neighbors who'd lost their job along with millions of others across the state.

So, this next generation of family matured along with Texas' "Gusher Age." Oil had at first seemed like an endless fortune-producing industry. Yet by the early 1930s, too much of a good thing had caused a glut that helped ravish the world's economy, and unwavering faith in the Almighty would once again be the open road through the stormy challenges ahead.

Chapter Four: Bridges

Walking up the four creaky steps of the local church, a somewhat inebriated Ted Anderson peered curiously into the wide-opened doors. Multi-colored folding fans waving lazily in the hands of every female in the congregation were the first thing he saw, as the balmy summer morning air in Port Arthur promised another humid day for the Texas Gulf Coast. Ted suppressed a chuckle as the fans looked like swarms of swallowtail butterflies, undulating their wings in the patches of yellow trumpet wildflowers back home in Meridian, Mississippi. Another glance brought another boozy grin, for the long-faced preacher at the pulpit brought to mind old Poncho, the family donkey that protected a goat herd pastured behind his daddy's blacksmith shop. No coyotes or dogs could ever kill a goat with old Poncho on duty. "Guess that preacher-donkey protects his flock, too!" Ted whispered to himself with a snicker before shushing any more such thoughts, for he wanted to walk in with a dignified manner.

He'd met a most amazing young lady the previous week, and she'd invited him to church. Though Ted didn't commit to the invitation then, as church wasn't exactly on his ten most desired places to go, he'd decided in the wee hours of Sunday morning to surprise her. The more drinks he'd tossed down with his buddies at the Union Hall after several hours of shooting pool, the more he was inclined to accept that invite. Ted had finally concluded around 4 a.m. to not beat around the bush with this woman. So, to church he would go. She was something special, and he had to talk to her, even if it must be in church. Besides, Ted reasoned, a little religion would probably do him some good. His thinking was a little fuzzy from the liquor, but his heart was set on seeing his future sweetheart right away.

After checking to make sure his pants were zipped, Ted thumped away the cigarette butt on which he'd been puffing and ran a comb through his wavy dark hair before stepping forward. He then casually strode down the center aisle, searching for the blond curls of miss Vida Mae Hughes.

Ellie Hughes was thoroughly enjoying the message of temperance being preached and having all of her daughters sitting alongside her. They were on the front pew, closest to the preacher's platform. This was her favorite seat, as Miss Ellie felt like the closer one was to God's Word coming forth, the better it would be seeded in one's heart. To her left sat Matie with her husband Jimmy Brent, Elsie, Madelyn, and her youngest, Willie Bea, who'd been born with Down Syndrome. Vida Mae was on her right, followed by the preacher's rather stuffy (and hypocritical in Ellie's estimation) sister, Hillary, along with her henpecked husband, Artie. Hillary wore the most preposterous red Sunday bonnet on her oversized head, pinned with a severe tilt forward. It looked to Ellie as if Hillary was scowling out from under a fire wagon.

With only a slight alcohol-induced weave to his long strides, Ted stepped lively around Hillary and wiggled his behind to wedge into the inadequate space next to Vida Mae. For a brief moment, Vida Mae was pleasantly surprised at the rather untimely arrival of this brash and ruggedly handsome young man, as she'd hoped to see him again after their initial introduction. A smile began to ease across her face at the visage of Ted's neatly combed hair and well-pressed dapper blue suit that matched his light blue eyes. Leaning his well-tanned face close to Vida Mae, he greeted her with a breathy, "Mornin'!" This was accompanied by an extremely stout and rapidly spreading vapor of Old Crow Rye Whiskey.

Horrific shock instantly replaced the budding smile on Vida Mae's face, and within moments this shocked expression had contagiously spread to most sitting there on the front pew. Even the pastor caught the vile odor of purgatory after a few ignitable seconds. As he continued to preach on the virtues of abstinence, his narrowed eyes began searching for the offending party.

Only a beaming Ted, smugly thinking his appearance in church would garner favor with the lovely maiden by his side, was oblivious of the pending firestorm. Hillary had already cast an evil eye upon Ted and would soon indicate him to the pastor, most likely along with an implied charge of guilt by association against the entire Hughes family.

"Get him out of here, right now!" Ellie whispered sharply to a terribly embarrassed Vida Mae.

The couple was a block away from church before Vida Mae grabbed Ted by his coat sleeve, and turning him to face her, asked sharply, "What's got into you, Ted Anderson!?!" Ted, who'd perceived all was not well by the furious pace Vida Mae had set upon their exiting the church, groped through the whiskey fog for a reply.

Vida Mae continued, "Did you think you needed a drink of liquor first to sit by my side? And in church, no less!"

Taken aback by the sudden emergence of a spitfire from the five-foot-three-inch previously soft-spoken beauty before him, Ted hesitated before speaking. A great sense of humor had always been his ally, so he resorted to this as a possible escape hatch from the flames of contempt emanating from his dream girl.

"Well, ma'am..." Ted began slowly as a preamble began to hatch through the mental bramble-bush of hooch. "It's like this. I tried three times to come into the church when I was stone sober 'cause I had something important to say to you. But every time I looked inside and saw that prepostru...perpossur..." he stammered clumsily before continuing, "that bat-crazy hat on the big gal next to you, I commenced to giggle like a kid at a carnival!"

Ted paused a moment for a quick glance at Vida Mae's face to see if his words so far were dousing the fire. But her expression was merely attentive. He thought that if she had a tail, it'd be twitching. Much like a patient lioness quietly watching a three-legged gazelle, whom the lioness knew she could pounce upon and devour anytime at will.

Instinctively interpreting the lack of fireworks during this pause as a glimmer of hope for redemption, he bravely continued, "I figured the only reasonable course open to me was to have a few belts first to dull my sight — you know, kinda like one puts blinders on a horse to get him past scary scenery — long enough to make it all the way down that aisle to you without cracking up!" Ted finished his appeal with a silly mock expression of childlike innocence and eyebrows raised almost to his hairline.

Though she tried to remain austere, a smile began to battle its way across Vida Mae's fair features at the hilarious conclusion of Ted's explanation. Finally, a burst of laughter doubled her over as she lost all hope of maintaining her composure. Ted dropped his faux innocence and laughed heartily along with Vida Mae. It was several moments before the fits of laughter would allow either to speak.

"One thing I have learned today about you, Ted Anderson," Vida Mae declared while dabbing the tears of mirth from both eyes, "is that you do have a quick wit and plenty of imagination! I have to agree with you about sister Hillary's hat, as I've had to glance the other way on occasion myself so as not to laugh! But gaudy hats just go along with Sunday church sometimes, and you'll have to promise me that if Momma ever lets me invite you again after this, you'll come in sober and giggle-less." Vida Mae's more serious tone was punctuated with her forefinger doing a one-cycle wag in front of Ted's face. "And what was the important thing you'd planned to say?" she asked.

Ted glanced away for a second. He wondered if the time was right to speak the subject that had been on his mind all week. "Let me first tell you this," he began with a sincere look, acknowledging within himself that this would just have to be the time to speak his heart, for he couldn't bear to hold it in another day. "You have my word of honor that I'll never pull a stunt like this again. The last thing on earth I want to do is to cause trouble for you or your family. I really thought I was sober enough to come see you, and I only made up my mind a few hours ago to join you at church. Reckon I got worried that if I didn't accept your invite today, you'd never give me another shot to be with you. And…well, that's what I'd hoped to tell you," Ted said with a sigh before hastily adding, "But under better circumstances, of course!"

Vida Mae waited for more from Ted, as his point was rather vague so far. She could sense that his strongly confident bearing, which was one of the first things she'd noticed about him, was wavering slightly. "Okay, I take that as an apology, and I forgive you. But do go on, Ted. I'm listening," she prodded."

Before we met, your Aunt Sis talked about you all the time to me," Ted explained, referring to Cay's older and widowed sister. "The more she talked, the more I felt like I knew you already, like you'd been a friend I'd known somewhere else, some other time. When your aunt finally introduced us last week, and we got to talk a while, that feeling became stronger, Vida Mae. You're so friendly and easygoing that I felt drawn to you from the get-go. What I want you to know is that I like you a lot, and If you're so inclined, I want us to get together more." Ted blurted the last line out hastily before he could ramble on any further.

Beautiful Vida Mae when she and Ted first met.

While they strolled slowly together along the sidewalk, Vida Mae contemplated Ted's proposal to start courting for a moment before responding. Sweet Aunt Sis had been ailing lately, which prompted frequent visits from Vida Mae. Aunt Sis told her niece about the strong and handsome young man who lived down the hall in the boarding house. Ted had been a thoughtful, gentlemanly helper to Aunt Sis, as he'd check in on her every day after work to see if she needed anything. They'd become fast friends, and Aunt Sis learned a lot about his background. Listening to Aunt Sis while sipping a cup of coffee, Ted's story stirred a chord of empathy in Vida Mae.

It seemed that young Ted's father died unexpectedly when a truck overturned on him. A big, strapping farm boy, Ted was just finishing high school, and his father's death devastated him. With the Great Depression in full swing, Ted determined to strike out on his own, leaving his family farm to his brothers. His mother sold the blacksmith shop in town and tearfully covered him in prayers. She gave him $2.50 from their depleted cookie jar funds, along with a bag containing jerky, extra buttons, and a sewing needle stuck in a spool of thread.

The heartbroken teenager hopped a westbound freight train, and while riding a boxcar, met an older ex-sailor who befriended him with tales of good-paying jobs awaiting them on the docks of Port Arthur, Texas. When an unsuspecting Ted was fully relaxed that night, the sailor sucker-punched him, knocking him stunned to the boxcar floor where he proceeded to pummel the lad unmercifully. This was followed by the cursing sailor grimly relieving Ted of all his possessions before pushing his bleeding body off the moving train several miles before the Port Arthur city limits.

A local family took in the bruised and disheveled teenager until he could recover. As the stitches on his face healed, Ted internally stitched a solemn vow upon his soul that no man would ever do him this dirty again. He would trust no one. He would strike the first lick at even a hint of aggression from another man. Every fight would be fought without mercy to the finish.

Ted did get work on the docks where he labored hard for however many hours available, sometimes moving cargo in the sweltering, filthy holds of ships for 24-hour shifts. Toughened physically and mentally, he rose quickly through the hard-fisted ranks within a few years to become Walking Foreman when only 22 years old.

Standing a muscular 6-feet tall and with bulging arms like the cartoon Popeye, Ted walked the docks with authority; and those cold blue eyes could drill right through any foolish enough to challenge him. By time Vida Mae met him, others in the boarding house and Longshoreman's Union hall avowed that Ted Anderson had the strength of a plow-horse, and there wasn't a man he couldn't whip.

When Vida Mae brought up Ted's stormy reputation after Aunt Sis urged her to meet him, a different side of Ted was presented by Aunt Sis. "I swear I've never seen such a tender-hearted and tough character in all my born days!" she'd exclaimed that morning while still concentrated on the shaw she was knitting.

"As I asked Ted more about what his momma was like, that usually loud, gruff voice smoothed and quietened down so, you'd of thought another person was answering. He sat down in the chair you're in now, Vida Mae, and spoke so lovingly and gently about his momma that you could've knocked me over with a feather! He has a tender heart under all those muscles."

Aunt Sis looked up from her knitting and leaned forward. "I saw a rare quality in this young man, my darling girl. You know that I am a good judge of character. While he spoke, I saw a young man come out of that tough cocoon with a considerate, unselfish, deep-seated love of his family that really touched my heart. I know he's a bit rough around the edges, but should the right woman come along..." Aunt Sis paused there, ducking her chin down to peer intently over her wire-rimmed bifocals at Vida Mae, "... he'd make a Jim Dandy husband and family man!"

With her aunt's words still fresh in her memory, Vida Mae looked steadily into Ted's eyes and replied, "Aunt Sis told me a little about you, too, and your suggestion that we 'get together more' will probably get her endorsement. She likes you and says you're a considerate person and that your rough ways are because you've endured some hard times. I can understand that, I guess. But you need to understand that I am a Christian first before anything else, and therefore I have to ask you if we have that in common. Right now, I don't know that about you, but here's the point. I don't expect any man who I'd consent to court to be perfect, with no flaws whatsoever. But he will have to be a believer in Jesus Christ and be willing to pursue living the Christian values as I have determined to do ever since I was a little girl." Vida Mae concluded forthrightly.

Ted did not hesitate to reply, "My momma took us all to church every Sunday, and I was baptized as a boy. Although I can't claim to have behaved as I know I should, I have no doubts about the Good Lord. I don't pray out loud, or sing hymns, or go to church like I probably ought to. But I am a firm believer in the Almighty, and I feel the same as you do. I could not be serious about any lady-friend or feel like we'd have any real, uh... future, if she didn't see things the same way." Ted took a slow breath before adding, "And if you'll give us a try, I'd like to start over by meeting you in church for the next service."

It seemed to Vida Mae that this handsome young man did have another side to him than that she'd glimpsed earlier that day. He seemed to have shaken off the effects of last night's liquor, as his conversation was very earnest and without any dullness. His candidness was most convincing.

By now, their strolling had taken both to the door of his boarding house. "Okay, Ted, I'll save you a seat at church on Wednesday night." Vida Mae said matter-of-factly, then added with a smile, "And I'll sit on the other end of the pew, away from Hillary's distracting hat!"

"Great! I'll be there before seven o'clock, and Old Spice aftershave will be my calling card this time!" Ted declared heartily. "Tell Aunt Sis hello for me, and let her know I'll pay her that ten dollars I promised for putting in a good word about me to you!" he joked with a chuckle and a wave goodbye.

The door to the boarding house foyer was open, revealing the staircase leading up to the first floor where both Ted and Aunt Sis lived. Ted quickly pulled off his tie, tucked it into his jacket pocket, and to Vida Mae's surprise, jumped briskly forward onto his hands. With legs straightly upside down above him, he proceeded to hand-walk up the stairs while whistling the tune, "Oh, Susanna."

"My, oh my!" Vida Mae breathed to herself, astonished at Ted's agility and coordination, as she watched him clear the top step. With another leap from his hands to his feet, he turned with a confident air and amused expression. Still whistling, he winked at her before striding around the corner out of sight. "Well, gal," she said quietly, "something tells me this won't be a boring courtship!"

Ted kept his promise and soberly attended church that week and every Sunday thereafter with Vida Mae, as long as he didn't have to work. He made amends with Miss Ellie and eventually charmed all the Hughes' family. Ted came to like and admire the pastor and even became friends with Hillary. She never quite detected the undercurrent of masked humor when he'd make creative and over-flattering comments about her humongous headgear. Vida Mae's sisters, especially young Willie Bea, would have fits of giggles during such moments. Even Hillary's husband displayed a few sideways smirks, identifying himself as a silent ally with Ted as the outsized hat brims often ruffled his hair or dislodged his spectacles when Hillary turned her head.

The courtship of Ted and Vida Mae seemed like a song composed in heaven to most onlookers. They were a handsome couple in appearance, and each complemented the other in a shared attitude of high regard that was obvious to everyone. Though they hadn't yet spoken it, both were madly in love. Nine months after the truce between them, Ted contemplated how to ask Vida Mae for her hand in marriage.

Before he could propose marriage, there was someone to whom he must first bid farewell. Someone that Aunt Sis did not know about. Someone who'd had an enormous impact upon his life.

Ted met her in high school a month before the Easter weekend. She'd transferred into the senior class from another school in the county and was introduced one afternoon to his math class. The only available chair was directly in front of him, and for an hour, all Ted could see and concentrate on was that lovely cascade of auburn-colored locks spilling down before his desk. As they came to know one another, Ted found her lightly freckled face and lively, bright-eyed approach to every conversation exhibited a personality to match that vibrantly-colored hair.

Although she dressed in very simple and plain clothes, it didn't diminish her inner beauty and magical charm. Ted was drawn to her feminine yet tomboyish ways. She loved pretty flowers and baseball, snuggling kittens to her cheeks and climbing rocky cliffs like a daredevil, watching theatric dramas or a Jack Dempsey prizefight. They were an item around school by Easter, and their friendship naturally ascended into a delightful romance.

Ted nicknamed her "Jackie" after the first day as he noticed the paper name tag on her blouse was partially torn, showing only the last name of "Jackso" —at least that's what he told his brother Johnny. Another secret reason was from a special day when Ted had asked her to be his fiancé. Jackie had agreed, then asked if they could wait until after graduation to announce their engagement, for there was some current trouble in her family. She'd refused to give Ted any details about the "trouble", mysteriously clamming up and looking away whenever he'd question her about her family.

When Ted at last reluctantly assented to wait, she'd put a little tin ring on Ted's pinky finger; a prize they'd found earlier while sharing a box of Cracker Jacks candied popcorn. Ted laughed and called her his "Cracker Jack Girl. When he shortened it to "Jackie," she smiled radiantly up at him and said that the ring would remind him of her love whenever they were apart.

Intrigued at her secrecy about her family, Ted asked school friends about Jackie's folks. No one had a clue. One weekend, a chance visitor to the Anderson blacksmith shop told Johnny that her dad was a destitute sharecropper who farmed some hillside land for an absentee landowner. Rumor had it that her dad was an alcoholic and deep in debt. That following Monday, as Ted was looking between classes for Jackie, he was summoned home after receiving word of his daddy being severely injured. Sprinting the two miles home to their farm, Ted arrived to find his mother and siblings crying bitter tears, for his daddy had succumbed to his gruesome injuries. Overwhelmed with grief, Ted kept scanning the crowd at the funeral, trying to spot Jackie. A few more dreary days passed while he helped his family get the farm and blacksmith shop in order before he returned to school. No one had seen Jackie in days. At the end of the day, Ted approached his math teacher to ask about the empty desk in front of his. After hugging the gloomy teenager before her and offering her condolences, his teacher informed Ted that Miss Jackson had abruptly withdrawn from all her classes at school. Nor did the teacher know where Jackie had gone. In an era where many kids dropped out of school to help work the family farm, schools did not pursue the child after the fact.

The next several days were excruciating to Ted. Everywhere he'd go, the empty places in his heart cried out at the torture of familiar places now devoid of the presence for which he yearned. His daddy had been Ted's rock, his hero, strong and gifted, always ready with a unique sense of humor and a word of encouragement for his son. A man to be proud of, highly respected in their community. Gone now.

Jackie was the first girl he'd ever truly loved and a trusted confidante within whom he could safely harbor his most private thoughts. A companion for life that would fill the days with sunshine and enthusiasm, unfailing love, and who would someday birth their children. Gone now in a mystery of the empty desk, as if she never existed.

By the end of that week, Ted decided to leave. Charging his brother Johnny to write him should Jackie ever return, Ted sewed the toy ring into the watch-fob pocket of his pants, which saved it from the scurrilous sailor on the freight train. That ring and his mother's prayers were all he'd possessed upon arrival in Texas.

***

Now, several years later, in his room at the boarding house, Ted contemplated the toy ring for one last time. His love of Vida Mae had healed the hidden hurt from those earlier years and consequently subdued (at least partially) the fire of his explosive temper, which was a byproduct of those devastating teen years. Ted strode slowly over to the open window that looked out onto the busy Port Arthur street below and dropped the tin ring, now tarnished with age, outside. "Goodbye, Jackie, wherever you are." Ted said very tenderly, "And may the Good Lord's face shine upon you always."

Somehow, this final act of closure of one phase in Ted's life made the opening of another seem easier, more appropriate. In the past months, Ted had found Vida Mae's presence very refreshing, much like the first brisk cool snap of autumn that lifts one's spirit after the long and humid, humdrum months of summer. She was everything Jackie had been and a good deal more. His previous concern over how to "pop" the big question to Vida Mae had flown out the window with that Cracker Jack ring. Ted's signature cockiness revived, bulldozing aside the earlier melancholy over Jackie.

Ted smiled as he dressed in his best clothes, buoyed by the confidence that he knew what Vida Mae's answer would be. He decided there was no need to rehearse what to say as he'd earlier considered. For a committed heart pours out its own timely poetry, beautifully undiluted by human design.

When next he saw his future bride's lovely face, he was certain the words would flow like the mighty Mississippi River at high tide.

Like a new bridge over that long-winding and treacherous old river, Ted felt he'd now bridged over from the prior hard times within his heart and into the promised land. He eventually would learn that, just as Moses and the Israelites of old, the promised land journey is fraught with trials and tribulations, of which the Lord uses to forge strength into the faithful —and to bring the prideful into submission.

Keeping a promise to his new bride, Ted quit working on the docks and severed some of the bad habits he'd cultivated while in that environment. Although he still partook of the fiery spirits on occasion, Ted did not indulge to the point of drunkenness as a tribute to the sobering effects of his Christian wife. A local construction company brought him onboard as a rigger, as his experience using steel cables and chains to lift heavy loads on the docks stood him in good stead in this new trade. His agility and ability to work at heights made him an instant asset to the construction teams erecting multi-storied steel structures.

Ted lounging on Cay and Ellie's porch.

Ted and Vida Mae were very happy together, and in the summer of 1937, their marriage was supremely blessed by the birth of a healthy baby girl, Norma Jean. The new daddy was overwhelmed with delight as he held his daughter for the first time. All things of prior importance to young Ted took a back seat as the enormity of God's blessings within this tiny bundle of life flooded his soul. Ted turned his back on those in the delivery room as he walked around with his face riveted upon his daughter, for he'd been raised believing that a man did not let others see him cry. The only words he could speak was a wholehearted prayer of three words whispered over and over again; "Thank You, Lord!"

About this same time, Ted achieved "Top Rigger" ranking and was assigned duties on an enormous new highway bridge project to span almost 700 feet across the Neches River from Port Arthur to Orange County, Texas. The supporting steel structure which Ted would help construct rose a daunting 177 feet high —the highest bridge in the south. This was engineered to allow ocean-going freighters and U.S. Navy ships ample clearance both in draught below surface and conning towers above. The upstream town of Beaumont hosted the Bethlehem Steel Shipyard, which built massive offshore drilling platforms and aircraft carriers. A big bridge was needed for this big industry. It was an ambitious undertaking, meant to reveal Texas as the hard-charging world player in oil and commerce she was always destined to be.

Vida Mae appreciated that the pay was good for late 1930s Depression standards, and Ted's boss forecast generous overtime hours for his crew. Ted liked the project, too, as he was fully in his element. He found the construction aesthetics unconfined and boisterous. Men worked a man's job in the open air. All around him, workers swarmed over the bridge's rising skeleton, noisily welding and bolting hard iron in lofty breezes. Freed from the confines of the earth below, they had an unsurpassed panoramic view, enhanced by the ever-swirling flocks of seagulls that constantly fed on saltwater shrimp stirred to the river's surface by dredging barges.

Ted's natural tendency to show off his strength and athleticism flourished as the rigger crews' routines of risky high-altitude duties were pushed to extremes by the foremen. They had hard deadlines to meet. Construction management strived for favor with the local politicians, who promised the public a completed and operational bridge by 1939.

To no one's surprise, Ted responded to the foremen's pressure with obvious gusto, as if the ramped-up expectations were a personal challenge. More than once, Vida Mae heard stories of Ted's reputation for balancing on the end of an elevated steel beam while snagging another from a crane-suspending cable via a hand hook and pulling the swinging ton of steel into position by himself. Folks said he seemed oblivious of the dangers involved. Like a mythical Greek god hovering above his minions, Ted would laugh tauntingly at coworkers that refused to join him on his perilous perch without first having a safety line tied to their waist.

One morning, Vida Mae told Ted of a dream she'd had wherein it seemed the Lord was warning her on his behalf about the detriments of false pride. She tried to break through his habitual morning coffee routine and newspaper reading to tell him of her dream. Vida Mae pleaded with Ted not to dismiss the dangers of pride and the related risks of letting it affect how he performed his job. With the birth of Norma Jean, the reasons for sensible caution in perilous work were vastly magnified. Their daughter would need her daddy while growing up. Not a tear-drenched tombstone.

But Ted only gave her the usual confident smile. He admonished her not to worry, as he was sure of his capabilities—besides, what's wrong with a man enjoying a little humor at work, as the other guys' faces made him laugh when he'd pretend falling? Vida Mae's prayers became more frequent and intense for the safety of her husband after such talks. The recurrent uneasiness in her spirit that a reckoning was due for his hardheaded Anderson pride continued to haunt her. Local news revealed almost monthly that some workers had sustained serious injury or death related to the bridge project. The actual dangers evidenced by these accounts supported Vida Mae's assumptions that working risks were far worse than Ted expressed in their daily conversations. He'd laugh these reports off as 'Newspaper Stretchers' or point out that a few guys hurt among hundreds of workers wasn't bad odds.

Within the year, they saved enough to rent a larger home close to others in the family. The extra room would be needed, for Vida Mae discovered she was pregnant with their second child. A month before their baby was due, Ted was called out late in the afternoon to perform repairs on the lower level structure of the bridge. It seemed a barge's crane derrick had accidentally struck an area of the bridge, causing damage that needed to be closely assessed before the next morning.

Before leaving, Ted kissed his bride and patted her bloated tummy, saying, "Now don't have our baby before I come back tonight! I want to be the first to welcome him into the family!"

Vida Mae answered with a soft smile, "I promise not to if you'll promise to be extra careful. Me and our baby had a little talk about that a while ago. He told me that daddy had better have his hide intact upon the grand entrance into this world, or there will be some mighty loud crying every night for many years!"

Ted chuckled while grabbing his tool belt and hard hat off the wall peg next to their front door. Turning around, he exclaimed, "Yes, ma'am!" while flashing a sunny smile.

Ted paused in the doorway and, turning back one last time, said dolefully, "I wish I didn't have to go right now, Vida Mae. You are the most beautiful little mother I've ever seen. Being married to you is the only thing that makes sense in this whole crazy world. Don't see how I ever got along without you."

As the door shut, Vida Mae felt a slow tear trickle down her smiling cheek. Her husband's sweet parting words had touched the eternal wellspring of love deep within her heart, bringing forth a soft tear and a softer prayer, "Please Lord, watch over my husband tonight."

An hour after Ted left, Vida Mae was awakened from her nap by someone banging their fist on the front door. It was still good light outside, and she could see Madeline on their doorstep through a crack in the curtains. "Come in, sister! The door isn't locked."

"Vida Mae!" Madeline blurted the instant her head poked around the door. "I'm afraid I have some bad news, dear! We just got a panicked call from Ted's helper, Roland. He said they're looking for Ted and for us to come quickly to the bridge. When he returned from a break and climbed back up to where they were working, he found Ted's tools still there, but Ted's not anywhere around. Roland was talking so fast I could hardly understand him, but I did hear him say he's afraid Ted has fallen into the river!"

In a voice so calm she surprised herself, Vida Mae replied, "Roland is always high strung. Maybe Ted climbed down to take a potty break. Ted has our car. Has Cleburne come home from work yet?" Madeline's husband worked at nearby Neches Butane and usually got off work about this time.

"Yes, he's in our driveway next door with the car running. Hurry up and get dressed, and let's go! We'll drop off Norma

Jean at Momma and Papa's down the street."

As they drove up to the bridge, a dozen men in hardhats had gathered on the near bank of the Neches River. Red-headed Roland was in the center of the group. He was talking and gesturing wildly but broke off the instant Cleburne's Buick rolled to a stop. The expression on Roland's face, along with those of the other men, gave rise to a childish urge in Vida Mae to put both index fingers in her ears, like a little girl not wishing to hear harsh words. Roland dashed toward their car.

While still ten feet away, Roland spouted in rapid-fire fashion," We found him! The ambulance just left! Don't know yet how bad he is…!'"

Cleburne interrupted with a raised hand, "Hold on, man! Take a breath and back up a minute. Where did you find him, and did he fall in the river?"

Roland gulped in another breath and grasped both hands together as if trying to get a physical grip on his rampant anxiety. "Ted fell, all right! But not in the river. He landed on a passing barge. Right on top of a real big hill of sand they'd dug out of the river and piled on the main deck. And you know what? It was dried sand, probably dredged up earlier in the week, and the sun baked it dry. Lucky It wasn't wet-packed real hard, or Ted probably would've been killed! He must've hit that loose sand near the top on a slant, reducing the impact, and rolled down the side closest to the pilot's bridge. Otherwise, he might not have been seen, and the pilot wouldn't have steered over to us. What luck!"

"How badly is my husband hurt?" Vida Mae inquired with a shaky voice.

"I don't know, ma'am. He could barely talk when they loaded him on the stretcher after they stopped the bleeding on the side of his head. I overheard the ambulance guys say to be careful with his back, 'cause he didn't have any feeling in his legs," Roland said remorsefully, with downcast eyes. Then he added, "Tell Mister Ted I couldn't find his hard hat, but I put his tools in my truck. They'll be ready again when he is."

Touched by Roland's obvious concern for Ted, Cleburne said, "I think Ted knows you'll take good care of his stuff until he's back on his feet, Roland. Thank You."

Madeline put her arm around her sister and could feel her slight shaking as Vida Mae sobbed and prayed. Cleburne turned the Buick around and sped off towards the hospital.

Both doctors that treated his injuries were just as amazed as Roland that Ted survived such a fall. Neither were overly concerned at the multiple lacerations or the fractured collarbone, but they had grave doubts about the extent of damage suffered in the spinal region. His entire back was one massive bruise, and x-rays indicated severe swelling of muscular tissue along with a misalignment of vertebrae in the lower region of the spine.

However, the good news reported to Vida Mae five days after his fall was that Ted was slowly regaining sensation in his legs and lower back.

"Oh, thank God!" Vida Mae sobbed upon hearing of this improvement. She and everyone in their family and church had been praying that Ted wouldn't be permanently crippled. "Momma! Papa! Did you hear that! He can feel his legs!" Vida Mae gushed as Cay and Ellie arose from their chairs in the hospital waiting room. All three embraced in joyful family unity over this answered prayer.

"One thing I must make you aware of." the doctor began after their rejoicing and tear-wiping had subsided, "Is that we do not yet know the full extent of the damage in Mr. Anderson's back, nor to what degree he will regain movement. We shall take more x-rays when the swelling has reduced. But I believe there's a chance both the cartilage disks between the lower vertebrae and possibly the sciatic nerve suffered injuries that could prove to be permanent. Lower Lumbar pain may be quite intense for a time, which could either subside... or continue for a lifetime." This sobering news caused a long moment of awkward silence. No one looked into the eyes of another as each pondered the dire possibilities for Ted's future.

"Only time will tell." the doctor gently concluded as he exited the room.

Cay gently hugged his daughter, then kissed her on the forehead before holding her out at arm's length to look intently into Vida Mae's teary eyes.

"Listen to me, sweetheart. We in this family have faced worse prospects in our lives than this through the years. We've learned to focus all our hearts to trust the Good Lord for deliverance rather than allow ourselves to dwell on fear. You would not be here but for God's hearing our prayers and saving your momma's life. Remember this when the natural human doubts assail you through the dark nights that occur in this short life. Read your Bible daily; listen to the Lord's guidance as He speaks to you through scripture. Set your heart with all determination to trust and hope in Him. Praise Him without ceasing when you're so tired you just can't think straight. Thank Him many times daily, ahead of time, for his decisions on the tomorrows ahead. Be assured, we will be holding you and Ted and Norma Jean up in prayer, and Lord Jesus has never turned a deaf ear to us yet. He will not do so, ever."

Vida Mae fought back a sob, feeling the depth of her Papa's love in his words.

"You know I've never lied to you, that I love you," her father continued. "Believe me when I tell you that I'm certain the Lord has great plans for your life now and in the future. These difficult times serve the purpose of preparing and strengthening you for the days to come. They will develop in you the attitude, the outlook, and expectations of an overcomer."

His daughter squeezed his hand.

"Follow my instructions, and even if you should live 100 years, you will one day look back on this time of life not with anguish but as a priceless faith-builder. That's how me and your momma now see our past troubles. And remember how the Lord reassured you when, as only a little girl, you fearfully prayed for Matie's life after her bad fall? He will do so again, daughter. Trust me in this."

Her Papa's expression relaxed as he concluded, "I've no doubts you'll be okay, daughter. Your fervent prayers are effectual. Ever since you were little, you've had a natural gumption for God."

It struck Vida Mae that she'd never sensed such a powerful aura surrounding her papa as she did now. She'd just glimpsed through the portal of his intense eyes a deeper level of her father's heart than ever before witnessed. Vida Mae saw an iron strength forged in this gentle man through his terrible struggles 30 years ago in the race against death, against the horrific fears of losing the one he loved most in all the world.

His faith in God and this spiritual strength were woven together. Each fortified the other.

Vida Mae knew all along of the unique stability underlying her father's humble exterior. Still, she surmised it took several years of maturity on her part to recognize the true depth and value of this stability. If God had given her a choice, she would not choose any other man on earth to be her papa. This inherent strength within him imparted a surge of strength to her spirit. Vida Mae's soul settled into a rock-solid foundation that, no matter the outcomes ahead, she would face it all by doing as Papa and Momma had done before.

She'd trust in God Almighty.

And because of this, when the dust of battle settled, she'd still be standing.

The Highest bridge in the South, the Rainbow Bridge.
Photo credit: Patrick Feller
(https://commons.wikimedia.org/wiki/File:Rainbow_&_Veterans_Memori
al_Bridges_over_the_Neches_River1.jpg)

Chapter Five: Unbound

Standing in line for hours behind dozens of other volunteers at the U.S. Army recruitment center had been excruciating to Ted. Pain radiated in waves from his lower spine down the back of both legs, with the worst of it on his left side, just as it had for years. The last few civilian doctors consulted had been unable to help his condition and gave him little hope they ever could. He desperately wanted acceptance into the Army as an alternate plan, for America's best doctors and medical specialists had been drafted for the war effort. And he knew the Army desperately wanted more recruits now. News reports had shown early 1943 had brought a series of setbacks to the Allies in this devastating phase of World War II.

Rumors were circulating that the government recently lowered some standards for the entrance physical. Ted waited for the rollercoaster of pain he'd ridden the last several years to hit a dip where he could walk almost normally. Today had seemed to be that window of opportunity as he woke up able to walk without a severe limp and stooped posture. After standing in line, his back started the old familiar stabbing pain, and by the time he'd performed the required standing toe-touches, torso-twists, and walking squats, the pain was unbearable. He fought to keep from contorting his facial features, but it was obvious to others there was something wrong. The evaluating medical observer pulled Ted from the test exercises and asked him if he'd had a spinal injury. Ted avoided the question, saying his back was sore due to some recent heavy lifting at work.

This ploy did not work, and Ted received an "Unfit For Duty" classification.

Ted thought about his family all the way home, and the stark realization he was letting them down felt worse than his physical torment. Images swirled in his head of Vida Mae working as a maid and doing odd jobs at odd hours to make a buck. She had no choice but to leave Norma Jean and their toddler son, Gerald Cay Anderson, with relatives as Ted limped from business to business and job to job. Unfortunately, he was constantly turned down or able to only last a few days at work.

Then there were the sleepless nights of bedridden agony when his back flared up for no known reason, like some devilish Medieval torturer was randomly plunging hot steel blades into a chain-bound victim's flesh.

He'd been raised to understand that a real man provided for the needs of his family. Ted learned early in life that a hard work ethic was the trademark of Anderson men, and the great physical strength inherited through their bloodline was to be used for that purpose. His blacksmith father could swing a 12-pound hammer all day, and he'd won the contests of strength every year at their county fair. Ted's strength was also well known among his childhood peers, and there was never any doubt he'd grow into a stellar performer at whatever occupation he chose.

Up until his injury, Ted always had supreme confidence in his manly abilities. This shaped to a great extent his sense of self-worth, his value as a person. Ted's unspoken claim to exceptionalism, validated since youth, walked confidently before him like a banner-bearer and opened doors of opportunity.

It had become his identity. Perhaps too much so, it now seemed. For he no longer viewed a man in the bedroom mirror these mornings. For all intents and purposes, Ted considered his confidently-walking legs as severed, lying useless on the sandy bottom of the Neches River.

Clutching the sheets with white-knuckled hands and slowly pulling his thinning body upright amid rancid smells of the pain-induced night sweats, Ted only saw a pathetic cripple. Looking at the darkening circles under his eyes in the mirror's image, he remembered the agony of his daddy's death that had previously been the worse loss of his life. He now considered it secondary. To his way of pain-racked thinking, the physical grave was preferred to this. It brought a conclusion. The dirt filled in and the headstone planted while the living, though sorrowful, walked away with some hopes of dried tears on the morrow. On the other hand, the loss of one's identity that establishes one's purpose and the potential for significance is a slow death that grinds down the bones of hope.

Hope dies harder and steals more vitality from the soul than any other loss.

Diminished hope often causes one to question the significance of living. The sense of loss increased every day within Ted, and his world was steadily shrinking.

Vida Mae could plainly see this dreadful decline in her husband and glimpses of the old buoyant, jokester Ted were getting scarce. Most of these times were when the children played around him, and the daddy spirit in Ted would momentarily override the bondage of pain. She'd try not to let him see her worry and would hum tunes or talk of the kid's antics to keep his mind diverted. As his condition worsened and the diversions became less effectual, Vida Mae increased her prayers and quests for a new doctor or new medical procedure.

She refused to give up hope and was firmly resolved that Ted would not see her crying spells. Though his hurts and despair deeply moved her, she was determined not to give in nor wear down to defeat. "God is still in control," Vida Mae repeated often.

One goal that became a focus for efforts by late 1943 was an increased quest for a good job. Should she land a good full-time position, the steady income would buoy Ted's spirits. Their financial strain could be alleviated, and better doctors could be afforded to assess and treat his injury.

Vida Mae tutored her brother-in-law, Cleburne Thompson (Madeline's husband), in math and chemistry to help him prepare for advanced certification tests at his job in a refinery. She had aced both these subjects in high school and found the refinery's study material fascinating. One of Cleburne's coworkers heard of her propensity for these subjects and told her of a new Butane company hiring chemist trainees. Inquiring into this, Vida Mae learned the position required a two-year college degree to start. She had only a high school diploma. Immediately, she went to the Lord in prayer and felt led to apply regardless of this stipulation.

The morning Vida Mae prepared to apply, Matie's husband, Jimmy Brent, came by to visit Ted while she dressed. Matie would drive her to the Butane company as Vida Mae's car had broken down, and they had no funds for repairs. Just before they were to leave, Jimmy came out of the bedroom and solemnly motioned Vida Mae to step out to the back porch. Sensing something was wrong, she asked him, "What's the matter?" before he could finish lighting a cigarette.

"Vida Mae, you know a man can only take so much pain before it clouds normally good judgment," he began in a direct manner. "I've known Ted for several years and he's as strong as they come in every way. But I believe he's about reached his limit of endurance." Jimmy looked like someone skirting around giving some bad news.

Vida Mae suppressed a gnawing sense of dread and stated, "All right, I've seen some evidence of this, too, Jimmy. What are you suggesting we do now?"

"I'm not sure exactly how to say this," Jimmy began hesitantly, "but you've got to understand that a man can only take just so much…"

"You already said that!" Vida Mae interrupted briskly, then caught her breath and ran a nervous hand through her hair. "I'm sorry, Jimmy, I don't want to seem rude. I know my husband's in a bad way, but please, please get to the point!"

Jimmy thumped aside the barely-smoked cigarette, straightened his shoulders, and replied, "Hide the guns."

***

The Butane Company's personnel office felt like the inside of an iceberg to Vida Mae as she sat reading her pocket Bible while awaiting an interview. Nine other job seekers had completed applications after taking the Basic Chemistry Entrance Exam. All but Vida Mae had interviewed and exited the building, leaving her alone to shiver in the exquisite leather and brass-buttoned chair.

It wasn't just the powerful air conditioner that gave her goosebumps, for she'd been chilled with the concept of losing her husband after Jimmy Brent's visit. She'd gone into another room and down upon her knees when Jimmy left and poured out her heart to God, pleading for mercy. Little Norma Jean had walked in and without saying a word, knelt next to her mother and clasped hands before offering her own sweet prayers for her daddy. She was so calm in demeanor that it helped settle Vida Mae's emotions. At that moment, Norma Jean reminded Vida Mae of herself when, as a child, she'd heard the assuring voice of the Lord about Matie's deliverance.

The knowledge of a job would relieve much of Ted's stress, and Vida Mae had faith the Good Lord would intervene to help those who trust Him. She kissed Ted and set out, determined to land the job with The Butane Company. The lack of college would just have to be overcome...somehow.

"Mrs. Anderson?" The receptionist's voice startled Vida Mae. "Step in here, please. Mr. Doran will see you now."

"I'll cut right to the chase, Mrs. Anderson," began the personnel manager. "This position requires completion of college-level chemistry, and your papers indicate you've no college background. Am I right?"

"Before I clarify that, Mr. Doran, would you please tell me my score on the test?" Vida Mae asked in a surprisingly calm voice for such a high-stakes scenario.

After shuffling some papers, Mr. Doran pulled a single pink page from the pile on his desk and lowered his bifocal glasses to study the print. After what seemed an eternity to Vida Mae, he lowered the paper to his lap and took off his glasses, twirling them by one earpiece, considering his words of response carefully.

"You've scored the highest grade than that of any other applicant, Mrs. Anderson, which makes my decision a bit complicated. Our training will be intense, and the chosen employee must be able to accurately absorb every detail for the sake of safety in running analysis on chemical batches. This score indicates you'd be suited for the job. Can you suggest how we can circumvent your lack of formal education as this job description requires? Corporate management will surely see this as a valid concern." Mr. Doran's body language was communicating a lean towards rejection.

Vida Mae paused before answering and thought of Ted, Norma Jean, and little Gerald. She thought of her fears as she'd hid Ted's pistol and shotgun. She brushed those fears aside with a conscious effort and thought, instead, of how God's promises and faithfulness were displayed all through the Bible and her family's history. He hadn't failed them yet. Vida Mae felt confident He wouldn't do so now.

With a budding smile, she thought of how excited Ted will be over her new job. After a quick mental "Thank You, Lord, for what you're doing right now!" she squared her shoulders and said simply, "Mr. Doran, if you'll just give me a chance, I know I can do the job and do it well. You'll see. I'll make you a good, reliable employee."

Mr. Doran saw the determination in her eyes and made up his mind. "Here are some papers for you to fill out tonight. Bring them back with you. Be here at the front gate at 6:00 AM tomorrow morning. Wear pants and a long-sleeved shirt. Lou, our lab foreman, will clear you with security and fit you with a lab frock, gloves, and safety glasses. Any questions?" he concluded with a subtle glimmer in his eye.

Concealing the explosive exuberance within her spirit, Vida Mae coolly replied, "No questions, Mr. Doran. Only I do extend my compliments."

"I'm not sure why you'd compliment me, Mrs. Anderson. You're the smart one who's finagled me into bending the company's rules about job requirements!"

Vida Mae gathered her purse and paperwork together, arose from the chair by Mr. Doran's desk, and strode confidently towards the open door. Turning around, she gave him a bright smile and said sweetly, "I compliment you, sir, for being an excellent judge of character. Good evening, Mr. Doran!"

Ted watched cynically as his wife ambled with slumping

shoulders into their bedroom after the interview. She removed her short-waisted jacket and sat disconsolately on the bed with eyes downcast. "They turned you down, didn't they?" Ted stated bitterly. "We both knew this would happen. Butane only hires college-educated goons for their lab. Everybody knows that. We're just country bumpkins from the sticks. These last few dimes in the jar will have to do for a while longer—but I guess we'll be borrowing again…" Ted abruptly stopped as he looked up onto a perplexing sight.

There was now a big smile on Vida Mae's lovely face, and her expressive eyes sparkled with excitement.

"I'll have you to know that some folks appreciate us country bumpkins, Mr. Anderson!" she bubbled girlishly. "And some of those folks work at Butane!"

"What!?!" Ted exclaimed, sitting up against the headboard through the pain that now felt insignificant. Vida Mae nodded vigorously in affirmation. "Well, bust my britches! You got the job!"

Vida Mae squealed in delight as tears of joy blurred her vision. She hadn't heard Ted emit that silly, hilarious phrase in a coon's age. It was a wonderful glimpse into her beloved husband's return to his old self. The uniqueness of expressions that defined Ted's personality just made a brief but refreshing comeback. The atmosphere around them seemed to lose its perpetual gloom as the spirit of despair swished away like a mythical vampire ducking out behind his evil cloak.

Within two months on the job, the Butane lab foreman gave Vida Mae a rare compliment. She'd completed some advanced analysis logs, and after close scrutiny of the documents, Lou muttered a quick, "Nice job." These were duties usually assigned to seasoned lab personnel, but he'd seen Vida Mae's potential and decided to test her acuity with the task. Her close coworker, Lois "Pinky" Smith, looked with an opened mouth at Lou's imposing figure fading down the lab's hallway and exclaimed in awe, "I've never heard him say that so easily before to a seasoned employee, and never to a new-hire!"

Lou turned out to be a gruff Cajun from the bayou country of Louisiana, and his no-nonsense attitude froze a scowl upon his swarthy face that intimidated most underlings. Even a casual conversation with Lou was rife with cuss words, and the frequent reprimands were delivered through locked jaws and swarming curses. To the unfortunate recipient, it seemed as if an eternally-aggravated hornet's nest resided in his throat. According to most lab employees, Lou's contrary ways would've fit in perfectly as boss of a prison chain gang.

But Vida Mae saw traces of good under his rough exterior. After the first week, he stopped cursing in front of her, and she overheard him say, "Vida Mae's the only real Christian around here! It's about time we hired someone that doesn't brag about going to church on Sunday while acting like a hypocrite every other day!" He had a particular aversion to Christians — why remained a mystery — and seldom missed an opportunity to loudly voice his atheism during any discussions involving God. To Vida Mae, this didn't seem consistent with Lou's respectful acknowledgment of her Christianity nor explain why he'd chosen to speak differently around her. If his disbelief in the deity and existence of God were solid, why should a Christian woman be deserving of a more civil voice? She hoped to have a chance to witness about the Lord to Lou.

Pinky was aghast at the thought. "Don't do it, Vida Mae! He won't listen, and you'll make him real mad! Lou's the sort of man that's mean all the way through," she declared with conviction.

"Well, that's just the sort who needs Jesus the most," Vida Mae replied.

The next morning, Vida Mae awoke with a high fever. She'd tossed in bed all night before taking her temperature at 5 a.m., which was 102 degrees. Ted tried to convince her to stay home, but she insisted on going to work. Vida Mae feared an absence on her record while still on new-hire probation could jeopardize her job. The salary from Butane was essential for their economic survival.

And most importantly, it provided hope towards medical solutions for Ted's protracted ordeal from his back injury. She had to go. Over Ted's objections, she downed two aspirins while standing shakily at the kitchen sink, and headed out the door. Norma Jean walked prayerfully by her side. "I love you, Mother!" were the last words she heard before opening the car door. Vida Mae wanted to reply with a blown kiss, but she was unsteady from the raging fever, and it took all her concentration to not wobble or fall while stepping into the vehicle.

Lou strode down the main south hallway, stopping at the doorway to each double chemist station jutting at right angles every 20 feet, similar to branches sprouting from a tree's trunk. Each short hall sported two chemists working 15 feet from one another with bottled samples, beakers, gas burners, a sink with water faucets, and various papers on a stainless steel countertop. One chemist was stationed near the doorway, and the other against the far wall.

When he stopped at the door close to Pinky's station to copy log analysis results, he glanced past Pinky and saw Vida Mae slumping at her station in an unusual posture. After calling her out into the main hall, Lou immediately saw that her face was extremely flushed. "What's the matter with you? Did you get too close to the Bunsen burner?" he asked sharply. When she lifted her bloodshot eyes before replying,

Lou reached out and placed the back of his hand on her forehead. "Oh, no! You're burning up, Vida Mae!" Lou burst out with a surprisingly compassionate tone. "Lady, you need to go see a doctor!"

"I had a rough night, Lou, that's all. Please don't send me home. I'm all right except for a little fever. Let me go wash my face in the girl's bathroom, and that'll bring the fever down, I'm sure," she pleaded.

Lou reluctantly agreed but posted himself outside the bathroom, waiting to check her forehead when she emerged. He began to write a security release for her to leave the building while he waited. Vida Mae's fever was too high for just a cool washrag to remedy. She was a very nice young lady in Lou's estimation, and he planned on insisting she see a doctor for obviously needed treatment. She would miss several days of work, and he was mentally forming plans to switch employees around to cover her absence.

Vida Mae began to cry while running cold water in her cupped hands and gently splashing her face and neck. She knew this wouldn't subdue a high fever, and a loss of one or more days on her paycheck would be hard to take. The possibility of losing her job was nothing short of devastating, and this would kick Ted back into the deep hole of depression. An uncharacteristic spurt of anger took over, and Vida Mae shook her fist at her own red-faced reflection in the mirror and exclaimed, "Stupid fever! You can't do this to us! You just can't!"

Between her anguished sobs, Vida Mae faintly detected a man's voice in song. Turning off the cold water, she wiped her face with a towel and cocked her head towards a far wall to better hear. The rich baritone voice was sweetly singing, "Jesus saves, Jesus heals…" As the volume increased from the unseen vocalist, Vida Mae's spirit increased with it. She unconsciously began to sing along, and with each stanza of the familiar gospel song (that her Papa loved), her vitality rose another notch.

Upon completion of the last notes, she knelt upon the tiled bathroom floor and prayed a flood of thanksgiving unto the Good Lord. Vida Mae rose to her feet, dried face and tears, and rushed confidently out the bathroom door.

Seeing Lou lounging against a nearby wall, she rushed over to him and said, "Lou, please go see who's in the men's bathroom." Lou looked up from the form he was writing, and a surprised expression spread across his ruddy features. Vida Mae's face was no longer flushed, and her eyes shone with a healthy sparkle. Without replying, he felt her forehead and was stunned to not detect any trace of fever.

"How did you do that? What kind of water takes away a high fever?" he asked incredulously.

"Just go see who's singing in the other bathroom, Lou. We can talk about this later. Hurry before he leaves!" Vida Mae said impatiently.

"One of the new janitors is in there cleaning the floor," Lou stated after reemerging from the bathroom. "He was only humming. Now, are you going to tell me what in Sam Hill is going on?"

"I know you'll find this silly, but when I heard him singing a hymn about Jesus' healing powers, I sang and prayed for a few minutes. I guess the Lord heard me and rid me of the fever, Lou, because I feel fine now. Is it okay if I go back to my station? I've got a lot to do before lunch," Vida Mae concluded with a radiant smile.

"Sure, uh, go ahead. I'll check in on you later." Lou said in a wondrous tone while scratching the top of his slightly-balding pate.

As Vida Mae strolled buoyantly away, Lou called after her, "Are you sure that's all you did in there? Just sang and prayed?"

"Yes, sir! That's all I needed. That's mostly what we all need in times of trouble. See you later!" Vida Mae said flippantly.

That night Lou's wife, a nurse, noticed his unusually quiet mood. He hadn't said more than a dozen words in two hours. Instead of giving her the details about his day, he asked, "Abella, have you ever seen someone real sick with a high fever, say 102 or 103 degrees, go back to normal in ten minutes by just washing their face?" Abella pondered this a moment before replying. "No, not really. Cold water may temporarily reduce facial fever a notch, but it's not a cure-all. Who is sick, and what's the cause of their fever?"

Lou shared the story about Vida Mae, finishing with a grumble, "That woman has challenged my belief that man is his own god ever since she started at Butane! She does it even when she doesn't say anything —" Lou broke off when he saw the smug expression on his wife's face. "And don't you start in on me, either! We agreed to respect each other's views about this. You can be a Christian all you want, and so can Vida Mae, so don't go doing that witness-talk stuff tonight. I just want you to listen and try to understand, 'cause I'm confused about what I saw with my own two eyes today. That little lady was seriously ailing one minute and healthy as a 'coon in a corn crib the next. You know I analyze everything on the job, and as a habit have always been that way. But this just doesn't add up, and it bugs the boogers out of me!"

Abella smiled knowingly and kissed Lou on the cheek. "If you'd settle down and logically consider what you observed on a short timeline, just like you do with a chemical mixture, you'd have to conclude this is a serious challenge to the theory of atheism. She didn't take any medicine, for you said she didn't have access to any, nor did a physician treat her. Even if these were available, a high fever isn't subdued in such a short window of time. The human body does not work that way. A good analyst would at least attempt to dig further for a logical conclusion. As your wife that loves you deeply and as a nurse, I recommend you try swallowing that famous 'Lou' pride and pray about it. Lots of people through the centuries have disbelieved, but after giving God a fair chance---which is not an unreasonable decision— made the most wondrous discovery of their life."

"Think about it, Lou, while I put the kids to bed. One suggestion: If you do try a prayer, be sincere and humble. Speak from your heart like you want our kids to do. Like loving fathers always want their kids to do."

***

When Vida Mae arrived home after work, Ted awoke from a nap to her singing "Jesus Saves, Jesus Heals" as she waltzed through the front door. A jubilant Norma Jean ran from the kitchen for a quick kiss before excitedly telling her mother about some earlier visitors who'd come to see Ted. Scooping chubby little Gerald off the hallway bookshelves where he'd perfected his often-practiced climbing abilities, Vida Mae's entourage swooped into Ted's bedroom. Ted looked surprised at her upbeat mannerism and quipped, "Guess that old ugly fever couldn't keep up with my pretty wife today!" Vida Mae laughed before telling him about the singing janitor and her swift recovery that so baffled Lou.

"I believe Lou has a lot to think over tonight, Ted. And I'm hoping what happened with my fever may just be the bridge I've been looking for to a heart-to-heart talk with Lou about Jesus!"

"That may be the case, Mother," Ted said thoughtfully, "but sit down on my bed here and let me tell you about a fellow Roland brought by today. He's a childhood buddy of

Roland's who has just returned stateside from the war. Both his legs and back took a burst from a German machine gun, and he's been medically released from the Army. Seems he has endured bad pains just like me for over a year as a result of a mangled sciatic nerve. Well, guess what? There's a new specialist in Orange that examined him last month and offered an, uh, unusual solution. This guy took the doctor up on it, and two weeks ago had a surgical procedure, and it worked. No more pain! Not now, not ever!"

Vida Mae's intuition sensed there was a caveat to the story that may inject a sour note into Ted's utopic introduction. But she decided not to voice any skepticism just yet. It was too refreshing to see Ted with his hopes buoyed.

After a long pause, Ted resumed. "The doctor cut the sciatic nerve just below a lower vertebra. In this case, he cut it before it branched to both legs. He is guaranteed no more pain, and the incision is already mostly healed." Ted added with an unreadable expression. "There is one lingering effect, and it'll take time to get accustomed to it…and that is, he'll not be able to walk."

"For how long?" Vida Mae asked while a chilling premonition answered the question as Ted squirmed farther upright against the bed's headboard.

"It'll be permanent, Vida Mae," Ted replied while looking down at his watch.

"Norma Jean, take Gerald, and you two go play in the kitchen. I'll be there in a moment to start supper," Vida Mae said in a quiet voice that sounded like someone else speaking. She realized her ears were ringing as if she'd been struck, then wondered why such an odd thought would intrude at such an inopportune time. She needed to be level-headed and to choose her response wisely.

"I'm guessing Roland's friend will be bound to a wheelchair the rest of his life. Ted, can that be what you'd really want? It would mean you've given up hope for a better doctor and a better solution for a mobile life such as you've always relished. And just when we're saving some money to reach out to others in the medical community? The Lord showed me at least one reason to keep hoping today, and I was excited to tell you so we could share some encouragement. Please don't be hasty in considering such a drastic surgery. Not yet!" Vida Mae pleaded.

"We called the doctor's office already. I have an appointment tomorrow to see if this is viable for me. It's right before you get off work, and I want you to take me. I love you and know you mean well. But this pain is worse than being permanently crippled. I've come to that conclusion; not at all easily, I assure you. So, will you get on board and take me?" Ted's steel-blue eyes reflected traumatic emotional struggles that broke her heart.

"I'll have to think about it and pray about it, Ted. Can I give you my answer tomorrow?" she asked softly.

"Sure. Take your time. Pray a little on my behalf, too, will you? My prayers feel kinda hollow."

The next morning, Vida Mae felt slightly groggy at work from a lack of sleep. She'd tossed and turned all night, unable to dispel from her mind the image of a downcast Ted, deprived of the mantel of self-esteem and permanently reliant upon others for basic everyday functions. Many others could adjust very well to a medical disability, as evidenced by an assistant manager at Butane who'd returned from the war with one arm amputated. Yet he excelled at work and kept an active lifestyle coupled with a positive attitude. She could not see Ted recovering in such a manner to the loss of his legs.

He'd be more like an adult wild eagle, thrust forcefully into a cage with wings clipped of the feathers that enable flight, forever robbing him of his lofty independence. Ted's inherent pride could never adjust to such a hard grounding.

Vida Mae wondered if the Lord allowed Ted's injury to bring him into a place wherein he'd be forced to deal with the sin of false pride (a term Ted said his daddy used when teaching his kids obedience to God). She'd seen a few times when Ted's confidence in his God-given abilities crossed the line to deviate focus from the Almighty and onto a self-serving level. He didn't exactly brag but seldom missed a chance to toot his own horn in a joking manner, which on the surface appeared to be merely a trend among the outdoorsmen of their culture. Vida Mae realized that Ted knew this was a weakness. During conversations about scriptures addressing pride, Ted got quiet and unresponsive.

Be that as it may, she knew God could turn Ted around from this destructive indulgence, but she could not bring herself to believe He would take Ted's legs away for a lifetime to achieve this. At least she hoped this wouldn't happen, for her old fear of the guns in the house returned as she pondered the possibilities after such an operation as he'd proposed. There was always the hope for healthy legs, but once the nerve was severed, so was that hope severed. Even without the physical pain, the spiritual anguish within that awful void of ever being free to walk again might tip the balance of reason one day.

The idea of coming home to find herself a premature widow and the children fatherless chilled her to the core. All throughout her prayers in the night and this morning at work, she'd felt led to strongly oppose the severed nerve solution. Then Vida Mae had contrary feelings of seeing herself as cruel and uncaring of Ted's constant battle with pain. It was a tug of war that must come to a climax, for Ted was expecting an answer. Besides, she suspected that he'd attend the doctor's consultation anyway if she followed her instinct to resist.

With that eventuality in mind, she decided to break a few moments before lunch and find Lou and ask permission to miss a few hours of work. She'd just seen Lou walk past their door a moment earlier. Then she'd call Ted to inform him they'd go to the doctor together. As she took off her gloves to unbutton her lab frock, a strong *No!* resounded within her. Taken aback, Vida Mae hesitated before quickly praying, *If this is your decision, Lord, please let us at least see what the doctor describes. Then if it's not your will for Ted to have the operation, speak to us both, so he won't think I'm just being stubborn.*

Receiving no answer to her prayer, Vida Mae removed the frock, and as she folded it to tuck under the counter, she detected a faint odor of gas. Turning towards the door and Pinky's station, she saw Pinky relighting her burner, which seemed odd to do just before lunch break.

Something wasn't quite right.

A lightning-bright flash erupted with a wall of flame spurting forth to engulf Pinky and the entire doorway. Vida Mae shrieked while instinctively throwing up her hands and bodily recoiling backward.

Before understanding what she was witnessing, the scene instantly changed to the building's outside gray brick wall with the red emergency exit door facing her 30 feet away. Catching her balance, she blinked rapidly as her eyes dispelled the briefly-lingering image of the bright flash. In a falsetto voice, she exclaimed, "What in the world...?!" in confusion before frantically rushing toward the door.

Though still disoriented about what had just transpired, Vida Mae instantly focused on one thing — she must get Pinky out of that fireball.

Abruptly, the emergency exit door burst open, tripping the electronic alarm bell as Lou and a dozen employees rushed outside. "Vida Mae!" Lou shouted in surprise. "How did you...?"

"Never mind me, Lou, go get Pinky!" she shrilled. "Hurry! She's in the fire!"

Lou spun on his heels, grabbed the sleeve of one of the men pouring out of the building, and shouted, "Get that fire extinguisher by the door and come with me!" Both quickly faded from her sight as they battled through the stream of bodies struggling to get outside. Wisps of dark gray smoke filtered out of the upper half of the doorway, becoming thicker by the moment.

Backing away from the exiting crowd, Vida Mae sat down on the concrete sidewalk and began to pray for Pinky. Hearing exclamations from the gathering crowd, she looked up to see Lou and his helper bringing out something heavy cradled in his frock coat. As they came closer, she smelled the sour odor of burning flesh and heard a pathetic whimpering.

"Here, Lou, give her to me," Vida Mae pleaded when she saw they were undecided where to lay Pinky. They gently laid Pinky in Vida Mae's lap. Upon releasing their grip on the coat-ends, bunched together like a hammock, Pinky's bodyweight shifted in a downward slide, causing her burned torso skin to peel off in thin-membrane sheets.

Horrified, Lou said loudly, "Emergency crews are on the way, Vida Mae. I think she's in shock. Care for her, please, until we get back. We've got to see if anybody else is still in the building."

Vida Mae nodded and continued her prayer with a flood of tears. An ambulance arrived within minutes, and they rushed Pinky off to a nearby hospital.

An hour later, Lou and his helper approached Vida Mae to assure her no one else had been injured and the fire was subdued. "Tomorrow's an off day for everybody while the company complete's its investigation and begins repairs," Lou said matter-of-factly. Then with a thoughtful expression, he added, "I didn't get to speak with the ambulance driver. Will Pinky pull through?"

"I don't know," she replied listlessly.

"How did the fire start?" Lou inquired.

"I don't know, Lou."

"All right," Lou said slowly. "Now, very importantly, how did you get out of the building, Vida Mae? I was only about 50 feet down from your station and around a corner when the explosion happened. I looked down there within seconds and saw the flame and smoke near Pinky's station before my view of the hallway was blocked by folks running everywhere. I led them out the emergency exit door. There's no way you could've beat me there unobserved. That's the only door nearby."

"Maybe she was already by the door when it happened, Lou. You were looking the other way," ventured his helper.

Lou turned a sarcastic face his way and said, "Even if she got past me unseen — which she didn't — then how did she open the door without tripping the emergency alarm, smart-aleck?!" Turning back to Vida Mae, he said, "Well?"

"I don't know."

Looking frustrated, Lou asked, "Can't you say anything besides 'I don't know,' Vida Mae?"

"I don't know, Lou. I really don't. One minute I was there by Pinky, and the station blew up, and then I was outside," she replied in a weary tone. "Can't you understand I've been wondering about this, too? The only thing I can figure is the Lord knows my husband and kids need me. He must have seen fit to spare my life. I didn't run out any door; I couldn't have gotten past the fire to do so. There's no other explanation, Lou," Vida Mae whispered, her blue eyes brimming with tears. "Not one."

**

As Vida Mae walked through her front door, little Norma Jean rushed to embrace her. "Oh, Mother, I'm so glad you're home!" she squealed with her face aglow. "Guess what? Daddy got me and Gerald to kneel with him and pray for you! Right on the floor by his bed. We heard about your job and the fire on the radio, so we prayed for everybody — but especially for you. And Gerald said, "Amen," so loud it made us laugh!"

Her daughter's excited recount of the afternoon buoyed Vida Mae's weariness, and she felt herself smiling. Hand in hand, they walked into the bedroom where Ted had Gerald tucked under his arm. Both were sitting up against the headboard and eating parched peanuts out of a bag. Ted's face broke into a wide smile upon seeing his wife.

"You're sure enough a sight for sore eyes!" he exclaimed vigorously. "We were worried sick when the news about Butane came across the radio. It wasn't until recently that Jimmy let us know you were safe. But he said Pinky was hurt real bad?" Ted questioned.

Vida Mae climbed onto the bed and described all that happened, including her miraculous exit from the burning station. Ted looked very thoughtful at this last disclosure and cleared his throat before saying, "I've been very selfish lately, and that comes from too much false pride. It occurred to me while praying that I've only thought about this hurt in my back instead of keeping you and the kids first. And the hurt of this false pride ego seems worse than physical pain. That's nothing but blatant sin. I couldn't see that before, but I do now after today. Thinking we could lose you to that fire shook me up, big time. The Lord and my family deserve better than I've been giving. I've told Him I'm sorry, now I'm telling you."

Vida Mae scooched over a bit nearer Ted and put her

hand on his.

"Please forgive me and know this; there won't be any doctor visit to see about cutting my sciatic nerve. You haven't given up on us finding something better, and I knew that. So I'm not going to give up either," he declared in a determined voice before raising her hand and kissing it. "Besides," he added, "If the Lord can save you from a deadly fire, He can save me from the fire in my back."

"Yes, he can, my husband!" Vida Mae eagerly agreed while kissing Ted on the cheek. "And you'll never know how happy this makes me. I'm sure, especially after what happened today, that the Lord has a great future planned for us."

Reflecting on all this, Ted said quietly, "I wasn't sure about telling you this, but I had a vivid dream while taking a nap earlier today. I dreamed I was playing a game of catch with a little boy, and he was throwing the baseball real good for his age. Just when I thought it was Gerald, he and Norma Jean ran across the yard. All I could tell was the little boy looked like me. Then I woke up to the radio blaring about the Butane fire. Maybe it's nothing, Vida Mae, but then again..." he left the thought hanging.

"That's what started my change in thinking about this sciatic nerve-cutting business. After all, such a procedure would end the possibility of us having any more children. All of a sudden, that seems a lot worse than living with a hurt back," Ted sighed in conclusion.

***

By the second quarter of 1945. the Allies had overcome through most of Europe, and the war focus shifted to Japan. Shipyards and industry were in full swing along the Gulf Coast of Texas as everyone sensed the momentum of victory was on America's side. The Butane Company had upped employees' hours to meet production flow, and Lou found himself promoted after winning an award for his quick response during the explosion several months prior.

Everyone commented on how this event must've changed Lou, for he seldom raised his voice anymore and never cussed. His signature scowl evidently burned up in the fire, for it was permanently missing, and a kindly smile greeted every coworker he encountered. He stayed in touch with Pinky, who was relegated to several years of reconstructive surgeries, and Lou headed up a monthly voluntary company fund to help her with expenses.

But these shocking changes were explained when folks learned Lou started attending church with his wife. Abella had switched to Vida Mae's church after hearing of her miraculous escape from the explosion. After a month of hearing from his wife about the wonderful services, Lou reluctantly agreed to come with her. His atheistic reasoning about life had suffered traumatically with the personal witness of a supernatural favor upon Vida Mae. First the vanished fever, then the incredible miracle of transporting her out of a building containing certain injury or death.

When he first saw her outside that explosive day, Vida Mae didn't even smell of smoke. Yet she saw Pinky enveloped in flames —and this witness enabled them to rescue her. Try as he might, Lou couldn't get this miraculous event off his mind.

Finally, he'd resorted to praying alongside his wife. She advised him to just relax and speak to God as he would to someone deserving of respect and absolute trust.

Lou took her advice and felt a peace settle over his uneasiness at committing himself to share his utmost private feelings — something with which he'd always struggled. He opened up to God. Without preplanning to do so, Lou found himself going to the front of the church when their pastor announced an alter call for those wishing to be saved. He later couldn't explain why. It was as if someone had led him by the hand and helped him repeat the sinner's prayer. He would tell folks for years afterward that it was during that walk his frown lost its footprint upon his countenance, and a smile of peace took up permanent residence instead. Abella joked that it was a wonder his face didn't crack like plaster and fall off at such a radical change.

He now understood what being "saved" meant, for he met the risen Savior in person that day. Lou felt his lifelong denials and sins being washed away. The cleansed man was a new man.

The crusty Cajun became unbound from the gruff and coarse cocoon that had constricted his personality. Along with a newfound joyous outlook, Lou made the decision to return to his home parish in Louisiana and share the Gospel. It was a calling that Abella enthusiastically agreed with, and they made arrangements with a tiny local church of the area that had just lost their pastor to illness. The timing was more than coincidental, and Lou felt confirmation and excitement for this new direction of life. The day he tendered his resignation to Butane, Lou pulled Vida Mae aside to thank her and offer her two gifts.

"Vida Mae," he began with a wide smile, "Thanks for being such a pure-hearted lady. Your differences shone out here like a beacon to me and to others. God has shown me through you that He saves more than just invisible souls; He saves lives. He opens doors to future days full of wonderful promise. I have here two things for you." He ducked his head, raised a small necklace with a golden cross off his neck, and placed it in her hands.

"This was my mother's crucifix. She passed away when I was a boy, and until lately, she was the only one who ever took me to church. I want you to have it. If my mother were here, she'd want you to have it also for being instrumental in her little boy's deliverance."

"Oh, how special this is," whispered Vida Mae, almost at a loss for words.

"Secondly, here is the name and address of Doctor Greenwood, who is a nerve and lumbar specialist just returned from the war. They're building a big hospital system in Houston, and he's already got quite a reputation for effective surgical innovations. Let him look at Ted's back. I heard the first visit fees with x-rays are very reasonable. In this envelope, I've included money to cover what his office told me they charge. When I first heard about him from one of Pinky's doctors, I felt the Lord wanted me to share this with you. I will be praying that this doctor will put Ted back on his feet."

Vida Mae's eyes welled with tears.

"Now, don't you start crying, or you'll get me to blubbering too! I'll say goodbye now, and we'll write you when we're settled down back home in Louisiana. Keep me posted on how y'all are doing, please." With that, Lou hugged Vida Mae and turned quickly away to walk outside where Abella was waiting in their car.

Vida Mae couldn't quite understand how a person could be so elated and sorrowful at the same time as she watched this ex-snarling bulldog-turned-saint walk away. "May God bless you and your parish, Lou. And may His presence glow in your heart all the days of your life!" she prayed with a final wave as Lou and Abella drove out of sight. Both were smiling.

***

Ted's surgery went better than expected. Dr. Greenwood

cautioned them in advance that although he had hopes of successfully reconstructing some of the scar-tissue damage in Ted's back, there could be no guarantees. Ted must remain in a wheelchair for at least a week after five days of post-op therapy. Only then could they assess what, if any, improvements would be forthcoming.

After the required time and daily prayers offered up from scads of family and church members, Ted and Vida Mae returned to Houston. Just before she wheeled him into the hospital, Ted grabbed her hand and pulled her around to face him. There she saw the old Ted-like confident smile, but with a new twist; an air of humbleness now softened his expression.

"No matter how this turns out, Vida Mae, I want you to know this. I will always love you, and whatever life throws at us, we will be all right. God's hand of mercy will assure us of that, just as he has done for centuries in His children. If I'm to be legless, I will still consider myself the most blessed man in this hospital. You and the children and all our family have convinced me of this. Any man who has such a God-fearing wife and healthy kids as I do is surely favored. But you want to know something? I believe we're about to get some great news!"

This proved to be prophetic, for Ted was able to stand, turn, and take baby steps with only minimal pain. Vida Mae used the payphone in the hospital lobby to spread the word to everybody back in Port Arthur. Her tears would not abate, and folks walking by misinterpreted her joy for anguish. She tried to wave off their expressions of condolence while she talked, refusing one gentleman's offer of his handkerchief and ended up in spasms of laughter at the comedy of it all. The doctor did affirm Ted's recovery and said he should be able to perform most standard movements, but he must limit himself in his lifting — no objects any heavier than a dining chair, and this was a lifetime restriction.

Ted ended up farming a peach orchard for a nearby landowner in Fred, Texas, for the next several years. His father had brought the first advance peach trees to Mississippi a generation earlier, so Ted had good knowledge of the practice. Norma Jean and Gerald advanced quickly through school, as both were very bright, and Ted spent considerable time teaching them math and science at home. The family bought their own home in Port Arthur, becoming independent for the first time since the year after Ted's injury.

Lou stayed in touch and always thanked Vida Mae in his letters for helping him become unbound from the deceits of atheism.

Ted eventually was lifting objects much heavier than a chair, and the old wheelchair grew rusty on the back porch. Every time Ted walked past it, he thanked God that he was freed from its confinement. And he thanked Him doubly for the lesson about the debilitating sin of false pride that the rusty wheelchair represented. They attended church with Cay and Ellie and others in the extended family, as God blessed their livelihood and spiritual development.

The whole family celebrated the surprise return of Vida Mae's cousin, Oceanus Tucker. Osh had returned from the war after being listed as "Missing in Action" for more than a year. He and two others had been separated from their unit on a small Pacific island while battling the Japanese. Bertie Tucker prayed night and day the entire time, refusing to listen to others as they'd remind her the Federal government often sent out MIA's ahead of time to prepare families for the Killed in Action telegram to follow. In her mother's heart, she just knew Osh was alive. Bertie felt if anyone could survive in the wilds, it'd be Osh. He was always as much at home in the woods as in their cabin.

Osh recounted how native villagers tried to hide the Americans from the occupying Japanese troops, but they had to live in the jungle most of the time. The Japanese poisoned all remote water holes. Osh showed his companions how to live off the land independent of waterholes, as he'd learned these skills growing up in the piney woods. He'd found vines similar to muscadines and edible plants close in shape to those at home. Ironically, just weeks before American troops retook the island, his two city-raised friends grew weary of small sips of water from vines or catching drops of rain from broad-leafed plants. They took a chance on a small, previously overlooked water hole and died in front of Osh that night, thrashing in agony on the ground as an insidious poison worked its evil on their weakened bodies. It was a gruesome sight that he never forgot.

World War 2 comes to an end.

Osh often declared he'd always known the Japanese Army was no match for his momma's prayers, the power of which he felt kept him safe through the whole ordeal.

World War II was won as the nation grew used to a prosperous peace. The next half of the Twentieth Century dawned before them like a promising new morning. The sun's rays shone on endless rows of clean white crosses in military graveyards, and the sounds of new birth echoed forth from hospital maternity wards of a free country trusting in the tried-and-true providential hand of God.

Chapter Six: Serving Windows

Ice cream parlors became popular across the South as the last dredges of the Great Depression faded into history. Booming prosperity from big oil advanced employment in all sectors, increasing incomes and allowing for extra family outings away from traditional home-bound meals. Folks gravitated to the cold, scrumptious texture of creamy refrigerated products to alleviate the discomfort of seven-plus warm months a year of south Texas living. Kids loved an icy soda float after baseball games, teens found first dates went down smoother with a shared chocolate sundae, and adults of all ages relished a good sugar-cone topped with the ice cream flavor of their choice.

Chain stores offering a "soft serve" variety of instant ice cream — made on-site in a refrigerated machine — sprouted up in busy areas to offer stout competition to the slower, traditional hand-scooped service found in drug stores. Everybody seemed to have taste buds specifically geared for ice cream.

Ted Anderson and his family were no exception to this rule. An idea struck him while sitting in their family car, listening to the slurping sounds of his family enjoying the products from a new business in town. Zestos had only just opened, but their lot stayed packed with vehicles as families walked back and forth to the windows in pursuit of desserts that appealed to all the senses.

A huge double-sided metal sign in the shape of an ice cream cone loomed on the roof with a realistic silhouette and paint job to match, luring passers-by into an ice cream frenzy. It was the visual equivalent of pouring blood into shark-infested waters. Several adults and two teens worked the inside, and their friendly banter with customers made for an enjoyable business.

Ted's idea took further shape while watching them work and serve in air-conditioned bliss. Asking his family to excuse him, he spoke briefly with the proprietor before walking to the back of the store and disappearing inside. He reemerged 20 minutes later and entered the automobile with an air of excitement.

"Vida Mae, "Ted began, "Didn't you tell me that your sisters Matie and Elsie were moving with their families to the new Texaco facility around Galena Park and Jacinto City?

"Yes, both Jimmy Brent and Bud Wilburn have been transferred there by Texaco. They've already started packing, and Jimmy Earl, Peggy, and little Jerry Brent have transferred their school papers. Elsie and Bud's three, Betty Jean, Buddy, and Mary Ann, are doing so today. With Houston widening the ship channel 50 miles inland, a lot of industries have relocated to that area. Why do you ask, and what's got you so excited?" Vida Mae inquired, obviously puzzled as to what Ted's Zestos meeting could mean to her sisters.

"How would you like to leave that smelly old Butane building and come work selling ice cream with me and the kids? "Ted asked with a wide grin. Before Vida Mae could reply, he continued, "And maybe with your nieces and a nephew or two as well?

"Ted, how…what are…" Vida Mae stammered before turning on the car seat to look squarely into his eye. "Ted Anderson, are you serious, or is this one of your silly jokes?!" she quizzed. "Because a store like this needs people with money to buy the land, build the building, and stock equipment and supplies. We don't exactly fit that silver shoe!"

"I'm serious as a hound dog with a ham bone. Zestos Corporation has a chain of stores starting in the South, and I just talked to the proprietor inside. He told me he turned down another Zestos store. It's being built by a landowner who agreed to a free three-month lease before charging a reasonable rent. The concrete foundation was laid before this guy had second thoughts."

"Why in the world did he turn it down?" Vida Mae asked with one eyebrow raised.

"Well, that store is located in Jacinto City, and his family is here in Port Arthur. The 60-mile drive was too much, so he took over this store instead," Ted answered.

"So, there's a store in Jacinto City just waiting for an owner?" Vida Mae asked with a bit of trepidation.

"Now, I know what you're thinking, Vida Mae. It means we'd have to relocate."

"Have you really thought this over?" Vida Mae asked calmly. She trusted her husband's instincts but had to process this information. "The only money we can raise would be from selling the equity in our home, and I'm not sure it'd be enough to start a business. Plus, what about my job or your peach orchard work? It will be starting all over, Ted, and with a new business in a community where we don't know anybody."

"Yes, my dear wife, but consider this; I can't get a good-paying job in the oil industry or any other around here because of my medical history. I couldn't pass a company physical. The orchard is a good job, but that land belongs to someone else."

"That's true," Vida Mae concurred, but she still looked unconvinced.

Ted knew this monumental decision would take a mighty push to gain consensus. "I want something that's ours. I've dreamed of something where we can work together along with the kids in a family environment. This business is right up the Andersons' alley. It's tailor-made for our outgoing personalities, and we'll have family nearby. Your nieces Peggy and Mary Ann could help us out after school. Norma Jean's almost 13, pretty, and smart as a whip. She'd be great serving the public. Gerald can help clean up and fetch supplies."

Vida Mae smiled at the thought of her nieces working behind the counter.

Ted took that as an encouraging sign. "Zestos will be a new family store run by a family that wants to contribute to the community. That winning smile of yours would be out in the open for folks to enjoy instead of hidden in the back of a chemical hallway."

Despite the fact that Vida Mae had worked very hard to establish herself as a chemist, she had to admit that venturing into a family business had appeal. Ted leaned closer to his wife with an intake of breath and a face that promised revelation, like a stage magician about to pull a rabbit from his hat.

"Your daddy, Cay, the man I respect more than anyone on this earth, once told me about the dream of a family farm he and your momma shared when they were young. He told me in heartfelt detail how hard they prayed before the Lord made it happen."

"Yes, and we were so happy on the farm, owning a piece of God's green earth," Vida agreed.

"This dream is much the same. And our time is now," Ted assured.

Vida Mae looked into her husband's lively blue eyes for a moment while considering all he'd told her.

"Vida Mae, the proprietor called the landowner in Jacinto City, and I'm driving there to meet him tomorrow — and if you can leave work early, I'd like you to come too." Ted finished his sales pitch with a quick peck on Vida Mae's cheek.

"Oh my!" Vida Mae exclaimed. "This whole situation is moving so fast..."

"Oh, don't you see, Vida Mae? This is the opportunity we need. Let's stop worrying and go for it!" Ted exclaimed with an expression like a kid about to unwrap a present.

***

Two months later, the last phase of construction on the Zestos building was completed. Ted coached Vida Mae on operating the handle of the refrigerated mixing machine to spiral the soft-serve ice cream onto a cone and into a pyramid shape with a curled flip on top. She mastered the art quickly and weighed the various sizes on a scale until she could work by feel, free-handing small, medium, or large cones that were precise in weight. She taught this to Norma Jean and Peggy along with Mary Ann in between stocking the storeroom and arranging equipment into an efficient workflow from soft drinks to ice cream machine to flavored syrup, and lastly to malt milk and mixer.

Ted paid some neighborhood little leaguers to go to every house nearby and record names and birthdays of every kid under 16 years old. Then he mailed vouchers for a free cone, redeemable on their birthday. Anderson's Zestos successfully opened on August 11, 1949 — Norma Jean's 13th birthday.

Cay and Ellie came to visit, staying the weekend with Ted and Vida Mae in their small rental house behind Zestos. Ted invited Ellie to taste-test their products as she was well known for her extraordinary ability to judge the quality of food flavors. Her famous talent qualified her as a finalist judge in the cook-off competition at Jefferson County's Fair each spring.

As Ellie sampled a dish of vanilla ice cream, Ted and Vida Mae watched her studious smile, which appeared after each small spoonful. Before Ellie announced her verdict, both were called out of the back office by Peggy to one of the serving windows at the front of the store. Ellie overheard Peggy explain that the elderly lady customer standing outside ordered a root beer float and a bag of potato chips but couldn't pay.

Upon receiving her food, and after scratching around in her black coin purse, she only came up with 12 pennies, along with two bobby pins and a cheap tin ring. The elderly customer frantically dug in her purse again, exclaiming, "Oh, I know I had more than this last night! My daughter must've gotten some out this morning to buy gas. I'm so sorry!" Obviously distressed, she pushed the bag of chips back across the window's counter. Peggy looked at her Uncle Ted for a decision. But he demurred to Vida Mae.

"No, ma'am, you keep those chips and enjoy them. They'll taste good with that root beer float," Vida Mae gently said as she pushed the chips back across the counter. "And here's your 12 cents back—you may need it today. Now, don't you worry about this. You can pay us later whenever it's convenient. Thanks for dropping by for our store opening. Come back and see us again, sometime!" she added with a smile.

"Oh, I surely will come back. And God bless you, Mrs.— ?"

"Anderson," Vida Mae stated. "And He has already blessed us, ma'am, by making a way for us to open this store in such a wonderful community."

"Are you sure about this, Aunt Vida Mae?" Peggy questioned as she watched the elderly woman depart. "How do you know she didn't pull the wool over your eyes about being short of money? You might've just gotten cheated!"

Norma Jean and Mary Ann ambled across the front of the store after serving customers at the other window, drawn by Peggy's tone of voice.

"Maybe so, Peggy... maybe so," Vida Mae said with a thoughtful expression. "But when praying about this business, I made a promise to the Good Lord. During the Depression, I saw folks go hungry, and Papa always gave them what he could, saying the Lord provides for those who believe in Him and help others. So, I told the Lord that if it's His will that we open this business, I would never turn away anybody hungry, whether they can pay or not. I never could, and I never will."

"Why, that's awfully generous of you, Aunt Vida Mae," Peggy said, a bit uncertainly.

"It's the right thing to do. So long as we own Zestos, that's how this store operates. I'm glad you girls are here to understand this. Even if a customer seems to be lying about having no money, give them what they order and do it politely. Ted and I are in agreement. We'd rather chance being cheated than to do business any other way. Do y'all understand?" Vida Mae looked at each girl, and all responded with a nod.

"Good. Now let's get your grandmother's opinion on the quality of our ice cream." They walked from the storefront to the back office, and Vida Mae asked, "Well, Momma, what do you think?"

"Love the flavor and texture. It's creamier tasting than the Zestos product back home. Of course, I had to eat the whole bowl just to be sure!" Ellie said with a grin. "One minor suggestion would be to strengthen the vanilla flavoring a mite."

"Our ice cream is creamier because we use ten percent butterfat, the highest content of any soft-serve mix I could find," Ted explained. "Other stores save a few bucks by using either six or eight percent mix, but it's less creamy. And I agree about the vanilla. I've been experimenting with improving flavor by stirring a small measure of vanilla extract into the cans of ice cream mix. Too little, and it doesn't quite hit the spot, and too much produces a distracting aftertaste."

"It's admirable that you're experimenting with the extract," complimented Ellie. "That streak of perfectionism will help grow your business."

"Why, thank you, Miss Ellie. I called Adam's Extract company about this, and they've agreed to make a stronger version of their highest quality vanilla. I received a case labeled 'Anderson Special' and will test it on my next batch. Their representative assures me we'll taste a difference, so I have hopes of meeting our goal of serving the best ice cream in Texas," Ted concluded confidently.

Vida Mae beamed at her husband and turned to her father. "Papa, what do you think of our Zestos store?"

Cay had been quietly listening after finishing his own taste test. He put the empty bowl aside and looked up with a smile at his little group of family. Their healthy faces warmed his heart, and he said a silent prayer of thanksgiving before responding.

"Your store has a lot going for it, Vida Mae. Everything is clean as a whistle, and your wide-sweeping windows all around the front serving area lets people see the cleanliness and observe their food preparation. Nothing about their food is hidden. That's important to a customer."

"Thank you, Papa!" Vida Mae said, smiling.

"What do you think of our staff?" Ted asked.

The Anderson's Zestos store in Jacinto City, Texas. Circa 1950s

"Your employees are well-groomed and polite," Cay continued. "A friendly smile goes out with every order. That's very important to customers. I overheard your conversation earlier with those young customers. You treated them like family and teased them good-naturedly. I saw the whole family returning to their car and smiling. That endears a customer to your business as much as great ice cream and cleanliness combined." Cay glanced at his wife, who nodded slightly before he continued.

"Miss Ellie agrees with me that there's one thing that stands out, and it shall determine the long-term success of Zestos. This one thing deviates a bit from the sole notion of pleasing customers. Evidence of this one thing shows the results of your prayer to the Lord about going into business. That evidence is how you treated the lady who didn't have enough money."

"I reckon Vida Mae picked up her convictions from you and Miss Ellie," Ted said. "She had a fine upbringing."

Cay and Miss Ellie looked pleased. "Our Vida Mae is everything we could have hoped for in a daughter. And thinking of how graciously she treated that customer, I recollect the Lord giving us gifts that we can't pay for. I had nothing to offer in exchange for Miss Ellie's life 40 years ago, and her death was very near. I possessed nothing of value in exchange. The same applies to every person's life and our eternal soul. We can't reimburse God for the sacrifice of His only son — we can only devote our hearts, our ways of living, and in this case, our ways of doing business to honor Him."

"Do you hear that, girls? Mr. Hughes is sharing the lessons we live by. Never forget the Good Lord," interjected Ted.

"That's right, girls. Most businesses would have retrieved their product and shut the window. Their focus is upon profits. You have assured success in doing business a different way, for you're focused on honoring and pleasing God."

Cay hesitated a moment to let this powerful concept sink in. "In other words, y'all are giving out much more than good food through those serving windows. You are serving love to an entire community, and the profits will be everlasting." He looked steadily into Vida Mae and Ted's eyes before adding, "I'm proud of y'all."

"Well, thank you. That is high praise coming from you," Ted said, pleased beyond measure at his father-in-law's words. "And now I better get back to work. You and Miss Ellie are welcome to watch."

Ted mixed the new vanilla extract into two 10-gallon steel cans full of ice cream mix, weighing 80 pounds each. He then grabbed two cans by their handles and was about to swing them off the floor, when Vida Mae's voice called out from the doorway.

"Ted Anderson, you're going to re-injure yourself!"

Ted stopped abruptly. "You're right, Vida Mae. I feel as strong as an ox, but have to pace myself," he agreed and hoisted just one of the cans into the walk-in cooler ten feet away.

At that moment, Cay emerged from the restroom. Desiring to lend a hand, he grabbed the remaining can as he strode by only to be brought up short by the unexpected and substantial weight.

"Oh Ted, this one's full!" he exclaimed in surprise, assuming those Ted lifted with such ease were empty.

"That's okay, Mr. Hughes, I'll get it," Ted assured him politely, not wanting his kindly father-in-law to strain his back. Vida Mae smiled while witnessing the love her husband had for her father, and also that Ted had experienced such a miraculous physical and spiritual healing.

***

Christmas Eve dawned bright and cool a few months later. Zestos closed at noon. Cay and Ellie, along with her brothers George and Billy Harrison and several others in the family, congregated in the back of the store just before closing. Ted drew out all the remaining ice cream into quart containers for the holiday dinner scheduled later at Matie and Jimmy Brent's home. The atmosphere was doubly festive, as the group celebrated Vida Mae's belated birthday from October 29, which fell on a busy Saturday at Zestos. Since the store operated seven days a week, there'd been no time for a birthday party. Vida Mae was 35 and looked ten years younger. There was a perpetual smile upon her face and a heightened exuberance in her conversation.

"Speech! Speech!" Ted shouted after Vida Mae blew out the candles on the lavishly decorated chocolate cake Norma Jean secretly baked the previous night. A small candied figure stood on top of the icing before a fudge-brownie wall and was artfully reminiscent of the Butane miracle.

"Oh, I don't know how to tell everybody how happy I am," Vida Mae blurted out while trying to suppress the tears welling up within. "God has been so good to us. Business is booming, and we have a great customer base. Some families show up every day. We're so busy our supplies can't keep up. Yesterday we received an electric bill that is 100 dollars less than expected. The meter reader made a mistake, but Uncle George says this is one of God's blessings to help us get by. I agree. Plus, I'm so thankful that Ted's back stayed healthy and has actually improved by leaps and bounds, even though he works hard over 12 hours daily." Vida Mae glanced at Ted, who jokingly flexed his bicep muscles like a circus strongman, causing giggles from Norma Jean and Gerald.

Gerald helps at the family store. Written on back is: 'Your everlasting friend. Gerald'

"Yet, the best reason for being thankful is known only to myself and the Good Lord — until now," Vida Mae said softly with a mysterious air and a sly smile.

She strode gracefully over to stand before Ted. With head tilted intriguingly, Vida Mae lifted her eyes, now shining with eager anticipation, to gaze upon his handsome face. His expression was comically quizzical. She allowed herself a muffled giggle before asking, "You know how that new 'Anderson Special' vanilla flavoring completes our delicious mix, making our ice cream irresistible?" Ted nodded in curious approbation along with Norma Jean and Gerald.

"We shall have yet another 'Anderson Special' next summer to further flavor our family. We're going to have a baby!" Vida Mae announced, releasing a tidal wave of pent-up excitement. The emotional dam could not contain her joy, and tears overflowed her cheeks.

After an energetic group hug among the females and a round of vigorous handshakes from the guys, Uncle George called the family to join hands. He led everyone in a prayer for God's favor upon next summer's child. After the "Amen," Ted excused himself for a quick walk to the restroom. His father had always instructed him to never cry in front of his wife or children, for a man represents the image of security to his family, and that image must be perceived as strong. Ted needed a moment in the bathroom, feeling overwhelmed and deeply touched by God's magnificent grace.

He looked back through the window of time and relived that vivid dream of throwing a baseball to a little boy. A son he'd not yet met but for whom he possessed a love unmeasurable.

***

"Uncle Jerry, what's a blue baby?" Norma Jean asked as she returned to the waiting room at St. Joseph Hospital.

"I'm not sure...why do you ask, pretty girl?" Jerry

Harrison replied.

"Because while I was standing at the tall windows overlooking the view of Houston, two nurses came from Mother's delivery room. One said it's too bad about the birth being a blue baby."

Jerry knew Vida Mae was sedated due to earlier complications per her doctor's last update to the family. He told Ted the baby's positioning within the birth canal was awkward, but for him not to worry. The doctor said he'd notify the family when delivery procedures were complete before anyone should be allowed to see Vida Mae.

His intuition was ringing alarm bells, so he asked his brother George about the term. A concerned expression replaced George's smile as he explained, "That's when a baby isn't breathing well. The lack of oxygen literally turns them a blue color. If the problem's not corrected, the baby may suffer brain damage and could suffocate to death. Let's step out into the hall and pray, Jerry. Then you go see Vida Mae while I check on the baby."

"If bad news is imminent, it's best Ted hears it from us first," George uttered with the trepidation of a preacher who'd notified parents of a stillborn child far too often throughout his years in ministry. The resulting heart-rending anguish burdened his soul like few other trials of life.

"Oh, Uncle Jerry!" Vida Mae weakly exclaimed as he peeked around the open door to her room. "They won't let me see my baby. Please find out if he's okay," she pleaded.

Jerry nodded before turning away and almost collided with a nurse carrying a tray. Before her stern face could speak an admonition for Jerry's unauthorized presence in the recovery room, he whispered, "Can you give me the status of her baby? My niece knows something is keeping doctors from bringing the baby to her, and she's worried sick."

The nurse's expression softened as she said, "I'm not at

liberty to say, but the doctor will be out shortly with a good report." As she continued down the hallway, she called over her shoulder, "He'll answer all your questions."

A now-smiling George walked into view and motioned for Jerry to follow him into Vida Mae's room. "How's my favorite niece and new mommy doing?" George exclaimed cheerfully. Before she could answer, George continued, "I hope you're feeling as good as your baby does. I heard him exercising his voice from three doors down, and he sounds mighty hungry!"

"Thank God!" Vida Mae exhaled. "Did you see him, Uncle George?"

"Yes, and he's fine. The doctor's cleaning him up and will bring little Johnny to you shortly. We will get out of your hair now; besides, I want to see Ted's face when the doctor tells him there's a fine, healthy son a'raring to keep him up nights and to start turning his hair grey!"

"We had a tough time of it for a while," the doctor began five minutes later, addressing everybody in the waiting room. "Mrs. Anderson lost a lot of blood, and the umbilical cord was wrapped around the baby's neck, strangling him. But he's a little fighter, and we got him untangled in time to prevent serious damage. He was kept in post-delivery long enough for us to be sure all vital signs are okay. I just left him with Mrs. Anderson. They are a good team already."

Amid delighted chuckles, the doctor continued, "Give them a few minutes together, Mr. Anderson, and then you can go see mother and son. Plus, you can help complete the birth certificate. We've put down all but his name — a six-pound, seven-ounce boy born this day, July 28, 1950, to Ted and Vida Mae Anderson. He sounds like a little guy, but he'll grow to be a big man someday."

"How do you know that, Doc?" asked Ted. "That's a much smaller birth weight than either of our other two kids."

The doctor folded his stethoscope and put it carefully into a pocket of his white surgical gown. "Because of the size of your son's hands and feet. When he puts a hand to his head, it covers his whole face. You'll see. He'll be a big fellow. Now it's up to you to make him a big man inside to match. If no questions, I'll say congratulations and take my leave now," he finished with shoulders slumped from exhaustion.

"One more thing before I go. You are a very blessed couple, sir. This could have gone badly. It appears that someone has your best interests at heart!" the doctor concluded with a meaningful glance heavenward.

***

Life in the '50s became one of prosperity and busyness, scattering some in the family to different locales and pursuits. Cay farmed his property in Silsbee. Farming remained a lifestyle as well for Ellie's sister, Bertie, along with husband Elton and son Osh. Matie and her husband Jimmy Brent's love was the cowboy scene, sponsoring local rodeos while keeping corrals of horses and FFA (Future Farmers of America) livestock. Every minute not spent at his new industrial job east of Houston was devoted to the cowboy way. His youngest son, Jerry, enjoyed the same pursuit along with big sister Peggy. Jerry excelled first at calf roping, then later riding rough stock and most rodeo events. He often took top honors as a finalist. Jimmy and Matie's oldest son, Jimmy Earl, liked rodeos but hitched his star to the U.S. Air Force. His letters arrived home from countries all over the globe as military service proved the ultimate adventure. Arvel Hughes moved to Arkansas with his wife and son Billy and daughter Edith. Elsie's two oldest moved to Oklahoma, while Mary Ann stayed home in Galena Park. Madeline and her husband Cleburne Thompson remained in Port Arthur with sons Greg and Ronnie—both accomplished athletes and local high school football stars.

Ted and Vita Mae continued devoting time and effort to the store. Johnny grew with the burgeoning business. Norma Jean, now known simply as "Sister," continued working there with Gerald and cousins after school alongside non-family employees. Customers thronged to the store as Zestos popularity increased. It became the launchpad for annual Jacinto City Little League parades and a favorite family hangout after Friday night football games.

Both Anderson teens were popular in Galena Park schools. Activities such as pep rallies, bowling teams, football, or baseball games increasingly detracted from core family time. Gerald and Sister were honor students, and college futures seemed imminent, spurring their parents to greater success at Zestos to fund the education denied their own Great Depression generation.

Now retired, Cay sat alone on his back porch, shelling peas freshly picked out of his garden. It was a cloudy, comfortable day sitting on his ladder-backed chair, listening to hens clucking and scratching the ground, foraging for insects. Miss Ellie bustled out through their screen door. The coil-spring squeaked twice as the door opened then banged shut behind her, recoiling with a short tap on the door frame before closing. The talkative young lady picking up Miss Ellie for church was new to the area. She commented on Cay's immaculate five-acre garden and casually asked what brand of tractor he used.

Cay replied in a manner in keeping with his reputation as a man of few words. Her jaw dropped when he answered with a nod to his opened, calloused hands.

"Did you borrow a friend's tractor, then?" she asked, still dubious of his simplistic answer.

"No ma'am, I turned over that field by hand with a shovel.

It wasn't too bad. Took me a season to complete and plant four acres of corn. I added beans, okra, and more vegetables to the last acre by the house. We're blessed to have good soil," Cay explained patiently and smiled at her astonishment over such a project without mechanized help. He wondered what her reaction would be to the degree of hard labor their rock-infested Panhandle farm of his youth required in the 1880s. He mused upon the cycle of generational progress, as remembrances of his father declaring how easy Cay's lot was as a boy working a farm compared to the youth of his day during the pre-Civil War times in Texas.

Hardships of life, it seemed, were eased in the advancing decades according to older generations of each era. With the physically evident truth of this concept, Cay rationalized that modern mankind in the "glitzy-Fifties" ought to be nearing a glittering state of Utopia by now.

But Utopia remained elusive. A nagging doubt in Cay's mind erased the smile, and an old favorite saying of his mother's came unbidden to mind: "All that glitters is not gold."

In spite of modern advances in medicine, surgeries, machinery, and other amazing inventions in modes of travel, of communications, and the exciting new hope of technology-induced futuristic space travel, something of great value was diminishing. That intangible value being lost worried Cay, not so much for himself but for his children, grandchildren, and following generations.

Looking at his spread upon the porch, woven wicker baskets of fresh-picked peas alongside Miss Ellie's big ceramic bowls for shelling, Cay's eyes locked on the half dozen empty chairs. They usually held his daughters or sons-in-law or grandchildren, and he could hear the echoes of laughter from days past as everyone joined in to shell peas or husk corn. Children were tasked with dumping the empty husks into Cay's mulch pile, and he could visualize them running gleefully and hear their excited shouts as they played tag around the house. A variety of conversations on the porch delved into the hearts of healthy or ailing families, developing communities, church events, schools, stores, new marriages, and new babies. And they shared encouraging advice for living truthfully and free under the promises of the Good Lord.

Occasionally, all would break out in a favorite gospel song, with lovely voices tweaked by at least one off-key — but enthusiastic — vocalist. The ensuing waves of laughter wove a golden halo of family love around every soul on the porch. To Cay's way of thinking, that kind of gold surely did not glitter. But its lasting value far exceeded that which was transacted through the windows of banks made of hard brick and cold mortar.

The barred windows of banks, Cay reasoned, were severely limited by time, rights of access, and amount of treasure, though the focus of society was increasingly directed there. By contrast, treasures served and received through the windows of loving hearts within the family of God have no such limitations. The valuables shared are unmeasurable, indestructible, and eternal. The former is temporary and subject to fears of loss, while the latter is eternally secure. For as Cay read in the book of Peter, believers have an inheritance incorruptible, insured by the Lord, Himself.

Cay worried his family was becoming too focused on worldly values. The obsessive pursuit thereof separated one from another and dimmed one's perception of truthful values. This caused a diversion of time away from the family core; and, in so doing, the intent of God.

Papa Cay Hughes on his beloved porch talking with his daughter, Matie.

He loved farming partly because it was family-centered. Though a hard-scrabble farm required diligent work from sun-up to sun-down, it was shared with all able family members. The meals and nights were sweet times of bonding one to another, as the family core was strengthened. Farmers and ranchers, by necessity, relied upon the natural concepts of God's established order and were enlightened of His awesome creativity and powers through seasons of plenty and seasons of little. Labeled "Mother Nature," it was on enormous display before them.

This was representative of life itself. The faithful farmer could better understand and withstand the ups and downs all people face. Some referred to farmers as the biggest gamblers on earth, surpassing Las Vegas casino customers. Hard weather events, bug infestation, varmints, erosion, fence failures, soil depletion, and market demands all appeared to stack the odds against them. But instead of relying upon blind luck, they learned to trust in God for wisdom to deal with challenges. Very importantly, the adults had time to instruct the younger generations daily on the key concepts of godly moral living, hard work, and persistence with courage.

Farmers knew healthy crops relied not on what was easily seen, as stalks may look green and stout. But the unseen underground solid root system is what supplies life-giving nutrition. Without a sustained source of nutrition, the stalk eventually withers.

It is much the same with people, Cay mused. Folks with a stable moral foundation are well-rooted to withstand the trials of life. This solid upbringing weaves the strong fabric of individual families and bolsters the strength of communities. And that of nations.

Cay envisioned these qualities woven into Old Glory, the American flag. It always inspired respect and prayers of thanksgiving from those who know its true history.

Scripture doesn't condemn the pursuit of economic success beyond what's needed for healthy living. But the "love of money" is to be shunned as the root of evil. Cay understood this to be parallel with the first Commandment about not putting false gods before God Almighty. Nor did he think farming was the sole method of wholesome work. Any honest trade, occupation, or business as a source of livelihood could be performed honorably and with obedience to the Lord's instructions.

When the love of one's work and subsequent monetary rewards or elevated social status became greater than the desire to honor God and family, far-reaching failures result. Cay knew of several well-intentioned men, including some faithful Christians, who'd crossed this line and confused their priorities. Lately, he'd witnessed this becoming a regretful trend in America.

Family time was considered secondary as a sparkling dollar sign sat heavily in the driver's seat. The reasons given looked good on the surface: affording college tuition for the young to enhance their economic future, a better home in a better part of town, a bigger and more reliable car, a secure retirement someday...and to fit the television-portrayed mold of "modern man."

These reasons boiled down to unseen priorities and unseen costs. Cay feared that by the time these costs came due, it would be too late to save a depleted marriage or wayward son or daughter — and eventually, a lost nation. The empty porch around Cay became an altar for prayer. He kneeled there to pour out his burden upon the mighty shoulders of the Lord.

Four short rings from the wall-mounted telephone by the kitchen door interrupted Cay's prayer. "Papa, we're swinging by to get you after picking up Momma from church, so get ready for a trip to Houston," stated his youngest daughter, her voice tense. Before Cay could ask Madeline the obvious question, she continued, "Joe called and said Osh Tucker has been terribly hurt. A tractor overturned on him and burned his leg so badly he'll probably lose it. He could die. An ambulance is rushing him to a hospital in Houston. Aunt Bertie's with him. Uncle Elton and Joe said she's asked for Momma to come quick and pray for Osh to live. Cleburne's honking at me now. See you in a bit!"

Ignoring protocol, the doctors allowed Bertie and Ellie into the post-op ICU after they'd amputated Osh's right leg just below the knee. It was questionable if the rest of his leg could be saved, but this would be determined within 24 hours. It all depended upon his body reacting favorably to the massive injections of antibiotics and recovery of the blood vessels and arteries.

Although he'd gone in and out of life-threatening respiratory failure after the trauma of amputation, Osh surprised the doctors and pulled through. Ellie prayed continually by his bedside.

Within a week, Osh showed remarkable results. His upper leg recovered. The tissue was healing, and circulation re-established. A smile spread across his face when Cay came to visit.

"Hi there, Uncle Cay. Where's Aunt Ellie?"

Cay sat in the chair next to Osh's bed before replying, "She's getting a bite to eat with your momma. You're looking good for a fellow that was knocking on death's door seven days ago. I've only heard parts of what happened and would love to hear the whole story from you, if that's okay."

"Sure thing," Osh said as he squirmed to an upright position. "I owed Old Man Connors a mowing job at his 100 acres spread down in the Hickory bottoms. He called and said his John Deere diesel tractor was already there with a bush hog on back and all fueled up. Papa dropped off me and Momma — she insisted on coming and brought a picnic lunch — before he headed to town for supplies. An hour into the job, I hit a stump while turning around by a deep ravine. The tractor swerved and bounced up, throwing me off. The bush hog hit the same stump causing the tractor to spin around before it fell on its side, pinning me down."

Osh took a sip of water from the glass by his bed before continuing. "I felt bones break in my leg, and then the smell of diesel fuel got real strong. The engine was still running, and I think a fuel line busted because it was spraying diesel on the ground by my leg. Momma ran over and tried to push on the tractor, so I could scoot out from underneath, but it was too heavy. Then the diesel fuel caught fire, and I felt my leg burning."

Cay couldn't help but squint in sympathy and reaction to

the agony Osh surely felt while being burned alive.

"That's when I knew I was going to die," Osh muttered with a faraway look on his face, as if he were speaking to someone in another time and a distant place.

Cay remained silent and sympathetic, allowing Osh to process the terrible ordeal.

"Can I tell you something, Uncle Cay? Something I ain't told anybody?" Osh asked seriously.

"Sure you can, Osh. I never told anybody about you putting your baby sister's poopy diaper in your momma's kitchen chair that day she sat on it, did I? You know I'll keep your words confidential," Cay said lightheartedly but with a steady gaze.

"Thanks, Uncle Cay. I didn't know anyone saw that," Osh said, flashing a grin before resuming. "For over ten years, I've felt like I shouldn't be alive. Ever since my buddies died in that jungle, but I didn't, it's as if I cheated them. We were close friends all through basic training. We looked out for each other. When they drank that bad water, all I could do was wipe their face and beg them to hang on. Both kept screaming and crying out to me for help while that poison was eating their insides."

"I'm so sorry, Osh." Cay reached over and put his hand on his nephew's arm, comforting him as best he could.

"My friends' deaths were slow and horrible. They made wretched puking sounds for hours. The jungle got quiet. Howler monkeys in the trees shut up their constant screeching as if they were some evil audience awaiting the finale of a ghastly Broadway play."

Cay inwardly struggled to remain stoic as the horror story unfolded, his heart heavy at what the young man had endured.

"Every night afterwards, I heard them call my name out from the dark jungle. I'd holler back that I was sorry they died while I lived on. And that I didn't know how come it happened that way. But no one was there, and the local islanders began to call me a name that means, 'He who talks to spirits.'"

"Even after all these years, some nights, I still hear them…" Osh's voice trailed off, unable to describe the tortures of a battle-bruised soldier whose spirit convicted him of treason. Osh knew it was an unjust verdict, but he could not shake off the demonic bulldog of his conscience.

Cay's heart broke for his nephew. While he searched for words to console him, Osh continued, "My burning leg felt like 100 rattlesnakes were biting me, and it was only a matter of time before the diesel spread to burn me up. But I was okay with dying. In a weird way, I was relieved it was happening despite that awful pain. I yelled for Momma to get away when she crawled next to me. She kept hollering out prayers and wouldn't listen. The tractor tires could pop with the fire anytime, and burning rubber would cover us both. I was good with dying, but I could not bear Momma getting hurt."

Osh paused. He dabbed at both eyes with his bedsheet. Cay respectfully stayed quiet.

"I begged Momma to get away. I told her nobody could help me. Papa wouldn't be back for hours, and the road's so remote there's no reason to hope somebody else might come along. We were miles from any main roads. You know what she did then?"

Cay shook his head no.

"Momma got off her knees and laid down beside me, right in the middle of the muddy stench of my slobbering and burning flesh and diesel fuel. It smelled like that infernal jungle during the war, where scorched blood and putrefying death stung our eyes. She wrapped her arms around me, looked up to Heaven, and told the Lord that she wasn't budging, and if he was going to take my life, he'd have to take her's too. She shook so bad I could hardly understand her."

Osh's voice broke into an emotional quiver, and tears dripped from his chin as he recounted this heart-rending moment.

"That's when everything changed, Uncle Cay. When she said that, I wanted to live, not die. 'Cause when you love someone, even if you're dying, you want them to live. Feeling this, all that old guilt left me. I was free. I couldn't figure out why, but the war inside me finally ended."

"Praise God," Cay barely whispered.

"I was screaming with pain, but I started praying with her. Before I passed out, I heard a truck and men's voices. Momma later told me a crew of lumberjacks were lost and driving around looking for the place where they were supposed to harvest timber when they saw the smoke and the burning tractor."

"Thank you, Jesus!" This time, Cay spoke his praise louder.

"They lifted the tractor off me and took us to Old Man Connor's place by the paved road, and he called an ambulance. They saved our lives. It had to be God's doing. Those guys were ten miles away from their logging site."

Both Osh and Cay looked into each other's eyes, sharing a bond of agreement and pure awe for the providential timing of God's mercy.

Reflecting later, Cay reasoned the Lord could've sent the loggers earlier, possibly saving Osh's leg and sparing much anguish and pain. But had he done so, Osh would remain under the constant torment of "survivor's guilt" from the war-time death of his friends, along with the resulting suicidal urges that deceived him into desiring death over life.

God arranged for more than a burning tractor to be lifted

off Osh by choosing this perfect window of time. His Divine mercy lifted the oppressive feelings as well. Via the beautiful love of his momma, who was ready to sacrifice her life beside him, the value of Osh's life in her eyes — and in the eyes of God — restored the personal value of the gift of life.

Love overcame guilt and freed the condemned.

The burden for his family losing touch with their God-given life priorities of faith and family was lessened to some degree after Cay heard Osh's story. God's mercy was not absent throughout the centuries recorded in the Bible or 45 years ago when Miss Ellie was dying. Nor was it absent recently in a remote wooded field, where a crying mother petitioned for her son's life in the midst of encroaching fiery death.

This renewed proof of love and mercy gave Cay more hope for his family's destiny than he'd felt earlier while kneeling on the back porch. He determined to continue the prayers, humbly adding thanks for the Lord's past miracles of mercy and for what He would do in the future.

Inspired by Bertie's example of pure and selfless love, Cay prayed with less fear and more faith...and more hope.

***

Multiple shades of red and gold leaves adorned the massive trees and carpeted the hardwood bottomland of Horse Pen Creek, making for an enchanting picnic site. Three sets of wide eyes gazed in wonder out the car windows as Ted's new Panama blue and pearl white Oldsmobile '98 rolled to a gentle stop by the creosoted-timber bridge spanning the spring-fed creek. As Ted and Vida Mae opened their doors, six-year-old Johnny launched out the back seat along with Pinky, the family's tail-wagging Alaskan Husky. They romped along the snow-white sugar sand creek bank with infectious joy, delighting the hearts of both adults.

The day trip was a combination of business and pleasure. Gerald and Sister worked the store while their parents visited Cay and Ellie to celebrate Vida Mae's 42nd birthday. She was plagued by painful rheumatoid arthritis, a malady she'd inherited from Cay. After an appointment with Cay's doctor in Silsbee, they drove by a 90-acre tract of timberland listed for sale close to Shady Grove Church. Although the property had no camp house or utilities, both fell in love with its beautiful woods, hilly terrain, and especially the naturally peaceful atmosphere. The sweet-smelling air serenaded visitors with relaxing sounds of birds chirping and gentle breezes in the treetops, as several thousand acres of commercial timberland surrounded and isolated this private tract from manmade distractions.

Ted helped his wife set the picnic spread while they discussed their two oldest kids, both now in college. Gerald attended Texas A&M. Norma Jean planned to leave the University of Houston and marry her fiancé, Walter Shuler, a Texas Aggie. They would live in College Station as Walter completed his time in the A&M Corp before committing to a two-year stretch in the Army. Sister would work for Humble Oil in nearby Bryan as an accountant.

"Johnny! Time to eat!" Vida Mae called out while unwrapping plastic knives and forks. "Hurry up, or we'll start without you!" She absent-mindedly thought about how everything seemed to be made of plastic these days. "Pretty soon we'll be driving plastic cars," she muttered to herself with a hint of disappointment that the steamroller of modern progress had advanced so quickly and squashed a lot of quality along the way.

Looking around, Vida Mae couldn't see Johnny nor Pinky's thickly furred and upward curled tail. "Ted, you can holler a country mile, so call your son. He's inherited your bad hearing, I'm afraid."

Ted's robust call flushed brightly-colored wood ducks from the creek 100 yards downstream. Yet even after bellowing Johnny's name a half-dozen times, there was no answer.

Deeply concerned, Ted's eyes scanned the forest. "You search south along the creek banks, Vida Mae, and I'll go southeast uphill. If you hear my pistol, I've found him. Take the pump shotgun. Fire two shots if you find him, and three if you need me. Load the shotgun with buckshot, not birdshot. And take extras," he added abruptly.

Vida Mae's building anxiety churned in her stomach. "Why buckshot?"

"Wild hogs. There are still a few bears around, too, though they've almost been hunted out," Ted replied, trying to sound calm. "Now, don't get too worried about critters. My concern is to find him before nightfall because it's easy enough in the daytime to get lost in these thick woods. A whole night lost out here would greatly lessen our chances of finding him..."

"What else were you going to say, Ted?" Vida Mae shakily implored. "Were you going to say, 'find him alive?'"

"Let's stop talking and get going," he replied gruffly. Ted remembered all too well the occasional lost child found dead by search parties after they'd spent days in the thick piney woods back home. Some were never found. He didn't dare mention this to Vida Mae.

***

Johnny ran through the woods with an exuberance of a suburban boy released into a wild fantasy world possessed with beauty enough to equal a Walt Disney movie. He ran without a care in the world and no thought of getting lost.

When he stopped to catch his breath, Pinky jumped an armadillo, and the chase was on. Johnny dashed after them with a wide grin at the armadillo's rambling hump-backed scrambles as he dodged sharply left or right while Pinky snapped at the top of his armored shell, constantly skidding in the loose leaves to correct for the armadillo's erratic course of flight.

When the armadillo dove safely into a log-crested burrow, Johnny laid down on the leafy forest floor, gasping for air and laughing until tears ran from his eyes. Upon sitting up and calling Pinky, who was fixated on the burrow with her snout inhaling great intakes of armadillo-scented air, his eyes swept their surroundings.

He realized he hadn't the faintest idea of the way back.

At first, he wasn't panicky. He chose a likely direction, then set out in a quick walk, thinking the creek was nearby. Within minutes anxiety hastened his pace, for he couldn't find the creek. Every wooded scene in each direction looked like the one before. None were familiar.

Breaking into a full run, he fell over a log into a patch of stickers, scratching arms and face, causing him to cry out, "Mother! Daddy!" repeatedly in panicked despair.

Hearing no answer, the sense of being lost and completely alone became the most horrible and devastating experience of young Johnny's life. Prior to this, his worse day occurred when their pet parakeet, Mickey Boy, flew away into the trees behind their home. Ted had a habit of letting Mickey Boy perch on top of his head as he piddled around the house. One day, Ted forgot he had a passenger and walked outside. Mickey Boy fluttered away in a burst of freedom, alighting in the branches of a tall elm tree. Though Ted and Johnny called to him repeatedly, their little blue escapee sat contentedly 40 feet above them with feathers fluffed, tweeting his usual "Pretty boy!" in response. Johnny heard him calling in the night, but by morning Mickey Boy was gone.

"Please help me, God!" Johnny cried over and over as he ran in wild abandon, stumbling over vines or downed limbs. Pinky ran too, oblivious of their danger, happily sniffing for armadillos.

"Please help us, God!" Vida Mae pleaded in desperation. Five hundred yards back, she'd found small footprints in the bed of a wet-bottom slough with several paw-prints alongside, indicating Johnny diverted away from the creek at that point. "Johnny!" she repeatedly called between prayers, focusing on the faithfulness of God and refusing to dwell on the consequences of Johnny remaining lost at sunset.

"Please God, find my son!" Ted prayed at the occasional stops in his zig-zagging search when he'd halt to listen for Johnny's voice or Pinky's barking. Though upset at himself for not keeping a closer eye on Johnny, Ted tried to shake it off, concentrating instead on every detail of his son's movements when last seen by the car. He was sure both boy and dog played away to the south, following the creek. Water always attracted boys. If they'd left the creek and kept moving, Ted was now in a likely area to find them. The woods were so dense in places that he could walk within 30 yards of Johnny and not spot him.

"Johnny!" Ted shouted loudly, praying his voice could hold out, and his search directions would be guided by the Good Lord. He plunged ahead through the brushy woods once more with a surprising pace for a big man, avoided low hanging limbs with an adeptness that would make a whitetail deer envious. His country-boy upbringing was paying off.

"Blam! Blam!" The two shotgun blasts echoed through the woods, stopping Ted in his tracks.

With a joyful shout of thanksgiving, Ted bolted towards a natural clearing, then backtracked to intersect the road. As

Ted approached the parked Oldsmobile, Vida Mae appeared by the creek with her arm around Johnny. His grinning, scratched face, wet jeans, and muddy Roy Rodgers cowboy boots told quite a story of adventure.

Ted thought he'd never seen such a welcome sight in all his life. Johnny looked unhurt with loyal Pinky by his side, happily wagging her tail. Vida Mae looked extraordinarily beautiful in her soiled khaki pants, red flannel shirt with leaves protruding in various places, and a radiant smile that seemingly lit up the surrounding trees. A purple bouquet of little wild orchid blooms peeked cheerfully from her shirt pocket.

His eyes were looking, but Ted's heart did the seeing, and he would remember the scene forever.

"Johnny and Pinky were a half-mile away, across that old slough where Uncle Elton used to make sugar-cane syrup," Vida Mae explained with an air of relief in her voice. "Johnny didn't wait to find a dry place when he saw me. He jumped in up to his waist in that muddy water, and Pinky followed! We both sat down on the bank, and he talked a mile-a-minute telling me about their wandering. He must've told me a dozen times how glad he was to see me."

Johnny looked from his mother to his father, his face awash with relief. He leaned down to pat his dog's scruffy neck. "Pinky didn't even know we were lost," the boy managed to say. "She was just happy to be chasing armadillos!"

"Did she run off?" asked Ted. "Is that why you lost your way in the woods?"

"No, sir, Pinky stuck with me the whole time. We were exploring and having a good time…until I couldn't figure out where we were."

"That's a good dog," Vida Mae said, joining Johnny in patting the trusty dog's back. "Praise God you are both safe.

Oh, and look what I found growing right where we sat — my favorite, these little purple wild orchids in full bloom all around. I couldn't help picking a few to bring back. I just love them!" Vida Mae said radiantly.

Johnny would recall her words in a poignant moment 61 years later, standing in a cemetery.

On the drive out, they stopped to visit Vida Mae's aunt Bertie Tucker and her family. Hearing of Johnny's being lost, Osh took him on a short walk to give some pointers about orientation. Ted walked too, with Pinky trailing alongside, wagging her tail and ready for another adventure.

"First, you need to know where you are and in what direction you're going before you set out," Osh began. "If you don't have a compass, take your bearings on the position of the sun, knowing it rises in the east and sets in the west. That gives you a rough idea of north and south. For example, if I'm going to Whitetail Ridge, that's about three miles northeast. Walking toward and left of the rising sun, I should be there in 45 minutes. Reverse this to return home, and expect to spend the same amount of time."

"But what if you're lost in the woods like me and Pinky?" Johnny asked.

"Well, if you're setting out into unknown woods, here's what you do. Observe the terrain at your base camp, such as creeks, dead or funny shaped trees, roads, pathways, side-hill, or bottomland — those kinds of features. Then choose a direction and note what time you start out. Now, this next part is important. Every few minutes, or when there's an unusual terrain feature, turn and look back the way you've come. Make note of all you see, 'cause that's your view when walking back home. The same glade you passed through while walking north will look quite different coming back there southbound. If going through a tough brushy place, break some of the brush limbs where the white broken part faces the direction you're going. Those breaks will stand out on your return. Check the time when you start back. If you haven't returned to base in the same time frame as the walkout, you're off track."

Johnny was all ears and soaked up the lessons, determined to never get lost again.

"Every now and then, turn and point in the direction you've just come. If there's any hesitation, and you're not 100% sure where to point, turn and backtrack right then. Make mental notes once you are sure again of your direction. This way, you'll be sure of where you are and how to return safely home." Osh wrapped up as he dug into a shirt pocket and offered a piece of gum to Johnny. "We're a few hundred yards from our cabin now. Can you find the way back?"

"Sure!" declared Johnny confidently.

"Then take off. Me and your daddy will be right behind you," Osh instructed.

The two men watched as the boy and his dog skipped ahead. "You know, Ted, while I was talking just now, I realized that's how a person gets unlost in this adventure of life," Osh said. "I figure a person has to check out where they've come from every so often to see if they're still true to the course God plotted for them. And if you're not where you should be, then backtrack until the right trail becomes clear again. That's what I had to do under a burning tractor not so long ago."

"I understand," Ted said. Then he looked thoughtfully at Osh and recalled he had to do the same thing during a rough time several years back. "I guess everybody faces a similar decision at one time or another. A decision of whether to continue on in a wandering course, even when you see it's wrong, or return, as we used to say in Mississippi, 'Back to the one who brung you to the dance.'" Both men chuckled in agreement before Ted observed Osh's good use of the artificial leg.

WW2 Vet, Osh Tucker, feeding a wild deer he's befriended.

"I don't mean to change the topic, but you sure do walk good on that wooden leg, Osh! Are you sure Bertie didn't eat too many hickory nuts when pregnant with you? 'Cause you look like you were born with that peg leg!" Ted joked as Osh outdistanced him to catch up with Johnny.

"Thanks, Ted," Osh said with a grin. "Don't know about hickory nuts, but Momma ate enough chitlins that Papa used to say it's a wonder I wasn't born with a curly pigs tail!"

Then he tossed over his shoulder, "And Ted, you didn't change the subject."

***

Zestos' serving windows continued to produce well

throughout the '50s and into the following decades. Sister and Walter's marriage was off to a good start.

Lovely Norma Jean graduates High School.

Gerald married his high school sweetheart, Sandra, during her senior year at Sam Houston State University. They tied the knot when he was about to graduate with honors as an aeronautical engineer from Texas A&M. He had a shaky start his freshman year, thinking college would be a cakewalk like high school. Instead of studying after classes, Gerald became hooked on rabbit hunting with some local country boys. His grades slipped to a low point for the first time in his life. In mid-November, Ted received a letter from the Dean's office that Gerald's grades were borderline. He might not advance to the next semester and, as a result, faced expulsion from the Corp of Cadets.

Ted put on his best suit after calling a Zestos customer who owned a foundry. Ted then sped his 1952 Chevy pickup straight to College Station. He waited two hours in the Dean's reception area before being allowed an unscheduled consultation. The secretary informed him four times that the Dean could not interrupt his busy schedule for an unplanned meeting. Ted informed her five times he would sit there until Hell froze over if necessary, but he would most certainly meet with the Dean.

With frustration etched upon her prim features, the secretary notified the Dean about his ornery visitor. "When Mr. Anderson kept calling me 'Madam,' I informed him my name is Mrs. Bloom and that he must refer to me as such! That, that, uh, uncouth man," she spat with a sniffle and upward jerk of the head, "said, 'I don't care if your name is Mrs. Fart-Blossom. Tell the Dean I'm still waiting to see him!'"

Their consultation was very interesting to the gracious and gentlemanly Dean of Texas A&M. Ted may have lacked a scholastic background but was nonetheless a wise and devoted father with a burning desire to see his son rise to his potential. This touching, though somewhat crudely stated declaration of authentic love, swayed the Dean — more so than Ted's ironclad guarantee, punctuated with intriguing expressions such as, "I'll work him like a beaver building dams in a petrified forest," and "Gerald will toe the line."

The Dean assured Ted he'd hold expulsion decisions until after finals.

Through Thanksgiving week and following weekends, Gerald shoveled sand at the Skyvara Foundry, working 12-hour backbreaking shifts. Ted assured Gerald this was how hard he'd worked as a young man, having lacked the benefit of advanced education or a skilled trade.

Gerald recounted these days often through the years, for though in peak physical condition, the hard labor at Skyvara was the most grueling of his life. His natural love for learning was greatly enhanced by Christmas, as sweat became the door-opener for a better view of the stuff that dreams are made of. Hours spent studying Quantum Physics were no longer drudgery.

He not only passed the fall semester but was awarded a medal the following May for Most Outstanding Freshman via scholastic merit in the Corp of Cadets. Gerald's family was present at this award ceremony in College Station, where the A&M Corp were standing in perfect ranks for the end-of-year presentations.

Ted avowed his expression of pride couldn't have been changed by a baseball bat to the face.

Gerald's heart burned with a desire to fly. This flame fanned brighter with every accomplished semester as he learned more about aeronautics. Some nights he dreamed of piloting a supersonic fighter jet through the stratosphere where the view was unconfined and the surge of power beyond any human conception prior to the present age. He was bound for the United States Air Force after graduation, and the whole world would be his cruising grounds.

An observer would instantly notice the dancing lights of this dream in his deep blue eyes whenever the topic came up. And the smile above his underbite-prone chin had more endurance than did his daddy's upon the medal awarding ceremony.

Gerald's first allure to the freedom of flight came into existence when only 12 years old. He'd been a finalist in the Junior Olympics Swimming and Diving Championships held in downtown Houston's Shamrock Hilton Hotel. Their new three-story high diving platform with a spiral staircase overlooked the world's largest outdoor pool. Upon Gerald's turn to practice dives before the competition, he ran up the spirals in child-like eagerness to a height that overawed some other competitors his age. The local pools he frequented in Jacinto City and Galena Park sported high-dives dwarfed by this triple-level platform. His graceful and acrobatic practice dives caught the attention of all onlookers and gasps of fear from Sister and Vida Mae.

The attending Houston Chronicle reporter snapped photos of Gerald in action. An article entitled "He's a Natural "appeared on the front pages of their daily sports section with an accompanying photo of Gerald in mid-flight of a swan dive. Gerald took first place in his division.

No other experience in his life so invigorated and elated Gerald as those few seconds in the dive where he was floating in the air, unconfined by all forces except gravity. Jet flight would be exponentially greater as thousands of pounds of thrusting power mitigated gravity forces. The last vestiges of physically confining restraint would be shattered.

Freedom of this sort, he thought, would be more than a quietly redefined intangible. It would be an explosive, quasi-spiritual experience.

Before Gerald's graduation, he underwent a pre-induction Air Force physical. It was discovered his underbite interfered with the fit of a pilot's oxygen mask. Since the military forbade altering aviator's crucial air supply equipment, he was not pilot approved.

Disguising the disappointment in his voice, Gerald called

his parents to say he'd be marrying Sandra and moving close to them after graduation instead of enlisting as planned. There were several job openings for an engineer in Houston. Vida Mae knew her son was crushed at having the dreams of flying grounded so abruptly and doubled the daily prayers offered on his behalf. Sister and several ladies at church joined her in praying for Gerald.

Sandra and Gerald enjoyed a lovely wedding, and their strong marriage relationship helped Gerald focus on being a considerate husband. But his dreams wouldn't die a quiet death.

He consumed every article on the rapid advances in military jet and missile developments of the early 1960s. America and Russia's Cold War spurred both superpowers into a heated contest for dominion of the skies— and the new frontier of space. Millions were spent on research and development as top-echelon scientists, engineers, and electronic gurus were lured away from private sectors and into government projects.

Lockheed Aeronautics — The Missiles and Space Program Division —combed the best universities for the brightest students in a nationwide talent search. Gerald Cay Anderson didn't escape their scrutiny. When they called, it took only a few moments to arrange a meeting. After strict security checks, Lockheed's R&D recruiter confided in Gerald that he'd be involved in advanced missile guidance systems projects. If current goals were achieved to target ICBM's launched from nuclear submarines more accurately, it would cross over into developing manned lunar missions.

Weeks later, Gerald and Sandra hugged a tearful goodbye to family. They packed whatever possessions would fit on the luggage rack of their foreign-made Hillman Husky. With four dinky cylinders revving, Gerald engaged first gear, pointed due west, and to the tune of the engine sounding like a bawling calf with hiccups, began the 2000 mile journey to Santa Clara, California, where Lockheed's R & D Center was located.

Sandra wept as home and family faded away in the rearview mirror. Gerald chattered excitedly about the wonder of a man dreaming of soaring hundreds of feet in the air, only to have the portals of providence fling open the heavens many thousands of miles high to spectacular altitudes. A descending full moon reclined majestically upon the western horizon as they drove through El Paso, illuminating through their windshield as if beckoning them to follow and not look back.

Though he wouldn't be a pilot, Gerald knew he was destined to touch the moon. His sleepy eyes focused on the targeted moon as their car sped through the night. They were alone on the straight black-top highway, with no other cars in sight. Neither had ever been on this road. The vast, clear, star-studded sky above seemed to encompass their whole world with a new sense of awe that transcended the physical. With his career aspirations focused on the moon, Gerald couldn't see a spiritual drought looming in the shadows.

Chapter Seven: Ain't Nothing

Jumping his king over two opposing checkers, Johnny grinned triumphantly at his grandfather. Cay calmly retaliated with a move that effectively encircled Johnny's pieces, blocking all escape.

"Don't clear the board yet, Papa. I'm still lookin' this over," Johnny declared.

Watching his youngest grandson scratch the curly light brown scalp over determined blue eyes, Cay felt a warm surge of pride for this competitive youngster. The boy had grown a lot since they'd seen each other last Christmas, and on this July 4th weekend, Cay detected a marked change in Johnny's voice. Norma Jean informed him that the Furr Junior and Senior High School choir director, Ron Nissen, recently moved Johnny to the bass section.

"He's quite busy with all the sports back home, Papa," Sister added. "Johnny lettered in football, won a blue ribbon at the Boy Scouts Regional swim meet, and struck out his Sunday school friends in a baseball All-Stars game," she bragged.

"Awww, Sister, that game was last summer!" Johnny blushed, interrupting her monologue.

"That may be, but Skipper Dunn's mom still mentions it at church. She said losing that game made him work harder at his batting," Sister replied. Johnny recalled the fledgling Oates Road All-Stars weren't expected to do well against the long-established and talented Greens Bayou team. During Sunday school, a week before the game, Johnny patiently endured some good-natured ribbing from three of his

Greens Bayou buddies who predicted they'd knock the "hillbilly" Oates team out of the park. The next Saturday, Oates beat Greens Bayou by one run, with Johnny pitching eight innings.

Pestering his mother to leave early the next morning, he wore his All-Star baseball cap to church. Discarding his usual shyness, Johnny strutted into Sunday school class with chest poked out and cap tilted forward in a brazen posture of victory. By some odd coincidence, all three of the Greens Bayou All-Star boys skipped church that Sunday.

Watching his own son pitching 40 years later, Johnny remembered this game as his best performance ever. He recalled being motivated by the presence of his daddy, who stood by the dugout that night, cheering every pitch in that notorious foghorn voice which some claimed rattled windows in the next county. Ted's appearance at Johnny's sporting events was a rare occurrence for the store was a demanding mistress, but it brought out the best in his boy. Skipper Dunn gained notoriety in the 21st century as the dad of pro baseball's Adam Dunn.

Another result from the Greens Bayou game was a boost in confidence for Johnny. He'd grown a lot that summer, worked out with others on the football team, and swam almost daily. Strength and endurance increased while his body matured. Entering the local gym early one Saturday, he recognized a lone figure of a lanky guy in his socks, shooting hoops at the far court. His name was Joe, and he'd bullied Johnny and others younger than him at school years earlier before being sent away to reform school for juvenile delinquents.

Joe didn't recognize Johnny at first, and by the time he did, he was in bad shape. Though Johnny didn't hurt him too much, both knew the bully days were over. Joe went out of his way to avoid Johnny from then on. Word of what happened spread, and both reputations in the neighborhood were changed. Joe was killed a few years later in Vietnam.

Johnny confronts a bully and comes of age.

Clearing the checkerboard for another game, Cay looked up briefly at his teenage grandson and said confidently,

"Johnny is a good lad. He'll be a good man." This brought a grin to Johnny's face. He dearly loved his grandpa, and this approbation made him feel taller. Papa had a knack for uplifting everybody in the family with simple words stated kindly. Each of his four daughters privately thought they were his individual favorite.

"I agree with you, Papa," Sister quipped. "He's my favorite little brother," she added with a smile. Before Johnny could point out she only had one little brother, Sister said, "Even if he has been skipping church lately."

"Mother's been working the store most Sundays, and I don't have a ride," Johnny mumbled, squirming in the overstuffed chair.

"Call me, and I'll take you. Your niece and nephew would love you riding with us," Sister replied sweetly. She was referring to five-year-old Terri and her three-year-old son, Scott.

Johnny acted like he didn't hear. Pretending to be busy placing checkers on the board, he tried to ignore a rising twinge of guilt. Like many his age, he was becoming more attracted to the '60s culture and less devoted to attending church. There, the music seemed old-fashioned, and though the preaching sounded okay, it was geared to adults and didn't ring his bell. There was no youth church. Adding to the boring factor, very few activities were structured for teens. Their ranks among the congregation dwindled.

Greens Bayou Assembly was a fine church, and Johnny loved the sweet people there. Sister Lucy Gates was a good example. She and Vida Mae were both visitors the same Sunday at church, but neither knew the other wasn't a member. By chance, they sat on the same pew, and neither knew anyone there. Both glanced uncomfortably at the other, wondering why they were not being welcomed. At the end of the service, a lady walked up and said, "Oh wonderful!

Two new visitors!" Both laughed about this for the next half-century and became friends for eternity. Sister Gates treated Johnny like her own son.

Like most houses of worship, Greens Bayou couldn't compete with the allure of recent James Bond movies, where hair-raising action with special effects, dramatic scenes in exotic places, fast cars, and faster women filled the big screen. Unlike Roy Rogers and movie heroes geared to youth in prior times, 007 had little scruples when it came to booze or sexual conquests. He didn't smile incorruptibly on Roy's sun-basked prairie but sought a life of danger, manipulation, and constant sexual seductions in glitzy casinos. He never acknowledged God.

Heroines of the new Hollywood forsook the Christian mainstay of virginal steadfastness before marriage, strutting a bikini-clad invitation across the big screen. Male theater-goers knew the fair maiden's bedroom door stayed unlocked and often ajar.

The entertainment industry's censorship door, closed for decades to the immoral contaminants of American youth, blew wide open, pushed by the same ill winds that eventually silenced the Lord's Prayer from public schools. "No Fault" divorce gained momentum. Husbands and wives were split, alienated by reversals in social norms to the approval of sexual promiscuity — deceivingly promoted as the "new freedom" by the moral midgets controlling Hollywood.

"True freedom," Cay had once told Johnny, "results when individuals make principled choices." He further explained that some choose to obey God with resulting peace, freeing the soul to develop life's purpose and meaningful relationships. Therefore, there is the freedom to sow and reap eternally good consequences. Others choose to ignore God and indulge in sin, with momentary pleasures evolving into a constrictor of the soul, like an unseen python squeezing out the ability to discern right from wrong, love from lust, and fading the light of life into abysmal darkness where lurks horrific consequences. Freedom is lost.

"Free is a little bitty word when said, but a great big reality when lived... or not lived," Cay concluded.

Like most teens, Johnny's hormones weighed heavily on his determination to make good choices, and the Hollywood-inflamed culture added to the burden. These hormones influenced the direction of his thoughts, overloading the Christian foundation of his upbringing.

Johnny guiltily thought of the advice of his football coach, "Smokey" Holmes: "Be careful how you look at women, fellas. The first look is okay, but if she's showing too much hide, don't let that second look yank your eyes out of socket. That's how you get in trouble." Sometimes Johnny turned away when he should, but other times it was as if both eyes were snared taut with fish hooks. *Those durn short-shorts some chicks wear don't help*, he reasoned.

"Do you have a girlfriend?" Cay asked.

"Yes, sir. Sorta. She works at the swimming pool. We like each other... but we're not going steady or anything."

"Do I need to get my wedding suit to the cleaners?" Cay asked with a sideways grin.

"Heck no, Papa! We've only started holding hands after my baseball game yesterday. And that didn't last long 'cause she said my hand was yucky. I pet a stray dog that wandered into our dugout. It didn't smell that bad to me. Girls sure can be picky," Johnny confided.

Cay chuckled at this response and remembered his own youthful confusion about girls.

"Pickiness can be a good thing. Let me give you some advice. Be very picky when you're about to get serious with a girl. Picky that she has strong morals and a heart for the Lord you'd want in a good wife someday. Don't settle for less. Then, if things turn serious and marriage looks possible, you don't have to worry. Remember this: you can't change anybody. Folks think if a potential spouse has some good points with a few bad, they can change the bad given enough time. It never works that way. Only that person and God can make real change happen."

Cay took a long sip of tea to let this sink in before resuming. "No one is perfect, so don't expect the impossible. But if her faults are tolerable and the good in a lady covers the essentials — and if you truly love her —then marry with confidence. Pray before and during marriage and set your own interests second to hers. Keep in mind the Lord has entrusted you with one of his precious daughters. This is a tremendous responsibility."

Johnny pondered his grandfather's words and hunkered down for another earful.

"Contrary to what's in the movies, lust is not love. Lust is only about taking. Love is about giving." Cay set his glass down and looked directly into Johnny's eyes. "Love your wife. Treat her like the most special lady in the world, and she'll be a wife worthy of high honor. And God will make you a better man for it."

"Thanks, Papa, I will," Johnny said quietly. "If I can get my hands clean enough!" he added with a mischievous grin.

Cay threw his head backward, shrilling a funny high-pitched chuckle, as he and his young grandson bonded together in the magic of laughter.

Johnny remembered years later that this was the last good talk he and Papa ever had. It came with a pang of remorse and the feeling he'd not held up to honoring Papa's advice.

Listening in to their conversation, Sister determined to share these biblical truths with Scott and Terri as they matured. Few men read their Bible as consistently as Papa. She attributed his morning and nightly routine of spending time in God's word as the primary source of his vast wisdom (he seemed to know a bit about everything) and his Lincoln-esque steadfastness.

Once, she'd commended him for this, along with his ability to accurately recall scriptures. Papa related how Momma's healing spurred his lifelong devotion to seeking God's wisdom. He'd formed the habit of mentally testing himself by closing the Bible and quoting several passages by memory. If he faltered, he'd pray before reading the passages ten more times, then try quoting again.

"Y'all read your Bible!" Cay smiled while waving goodbye later. Rays from the evening sun highlighted his silvery hair, giving the appearance of a light shining out toward their departing car. This scene stuck in Sister and Johnny's memory like a master artist's painting.

***

One beautiful evening, Jeremiah Caleb Hughes was picking okra in his garden. He likely was thinking about the timeliness of harvesting this vegetable, which became unsavory and leathery if left on the stem too long. Suddenly and without warning, a massive heart attack dropped him onto the rich soil upon which he'd lovingly labored for 30 years. Cay's well-traveled journey, begun in 1877, was now complete. Jeremiah Caleb Hughes went to his Father's house, justified.

Cay's life continued to produce good fruit. His clean footprints left lasting impressions on life's pathway of countless others living on after him, helping them find true direction in their own journey. Many years later, one of his grandsons wrote of Cay:

A quiet, taciturn man who preferred listening to

talking, my grandfather Cay was a man of his word, and not one of his words was a curse. I don't recollect (one of his favorite words) him being big on religion, but he had a deep abiding faith in God and lived by his oft-read Bible. This was the source of his strength, great peace, and the wellhead of that ubiquitous smile. Consideration was one of his best virtues, and he included everyone equally. My most enduring memories of Papa are not of a particular scene or word or deed, but just of the man in general, whose every gesture and soft-spoken utterance was an unconscious revelation of rare human character. His teachings by example carry down through the generations; a rich heritage indeed.

Seven months later, Miss Ellie, who'd not been sick since her healing from typhoid in 1908 at Shady Grove Church, began having chest pains. A nurse came out of the hospital examination room and into the hallway where Vida Mae and Matie were waiting. "She's experiencing heart failure, coming into and out of consciousness, but you may see her," the nurse said gently. "She's sedated now, and in her sleep, talks very lovingly to a Mister Hughes. I was wondering who that is," the nurse queried.

As Vida Mae and Matie sat on Miss Ellie's bed, they heard her say, "Yes. Mr. Hughes. Tell Lester and Willie Bea I'll be there." As Vida Mae caressed her cheek, Ellie Angeline Harrison Hughes opened her eyes, sat upright, and exclaimed, "Oh Lord, have mercy on me!" She then laid back, closed her eyes, and went peacefully home.

A significant family era passed with her.

Both hands were crossed over her heart. It struck Vida Mae that those hands were prayerfully laid upon numerous sick folks for 70 years to invoke God's healing, but with her last breath touched her own now-healed heart, broken since the day Cay died. The final gift of "the laying on of hands" was mercifully received by the giver.

Laying Miss Ellie next to Cay in the country graveyard, the gathering of family wept and hugged and smiled, for the ending of an earthly era was crowned by a heavenly reunion. A few noticed upon leaving a large, beautiful red-tailed hawk with the setting sun reflecting from his coppery plumage, circling upwards and gaining altitude until he was out of sight.

***

"I'm starting a Bible Quiz Team for the youth in our church," Sister notified her husband, Walter. Papa's example was one of the motivating factors for this decision. Bible Quiz consisted of competitive meets with judges who gave contestants a limited time to quote a given set of scriptures. It was a true competition that fostered biblical literacy. Although she'd returned to college after Terri and Scott were born, getting her bachelor's and master's degrees and a CPA license in accounting while working, Sister made time in her busy schedule to meet with and train youth in her house.

This continued for over two decades. Her teams made the national finals a few times, winning it all one year. Her son, Scott, coached his own Bible Quiz Team years later. Sister's focus never wavered from building upon the Kingdom of God. Her protégées bloomed from Bible Quiz beginnings into ministers, pastors, and evangelists, feeding God's word to tens of thousands well into the 21st century. One of her best quizzers, Jerome Tang, became the associate head men's basketball coach at Baylor University. Under his inspirational guidance, they were National Champions of the Big 12 Conference in 2021. Jerome still quotes scripture at will and coaches' moral character with even more finesse than he

AN INHERITANCE INCORRUPTIBLE

does basketball.

Norma Jean's spiritual seeds were sewn into very good soil.

NASA's Gemini and Apollo projects kept Gerald heavily occupied throughout the mid-'60s and '70s. He was an instrumental part of the team in a dozen American space shots. With a myriad of problems to solve regarding missile launch and abort programming, rocket stage-launching, flight simulation, orbiting, re-entry, docking, his department kept long, odd hours cloaked in absolute secrecy. This endeavor was both an exciting challenge and a strain on family life. The relatively few hours spent at home were mute on the normal spousal discussions concerning work.

Gerald knew he was shorting time with Sandra, young son Steve, and their newborn, David. He told himself they all would see it as a worthy sacrifice in the future.

Expectations were high that a successful moon shot would promote peace on earth via new technology, rendering military aggression unwise in light of swift retaliation from orbiting space stations. That was one reason America and Russia strove so obsessively to be the "first" in space advances. Conquering the vast unknown physics of space and how earthly materials and men could withstand the alien environment was a daunting challenge, but one Gerald relished.

He'd always had an insatiable curiosity. As a child, Gerald dismantled new action toys instead of playing with them, as most kids do. He had to see how the mechanism of the toy worked. Play came later. The celestial wonders drew his curiosity forth like a giant genie from Aladdin's lamp. It overshadowed all else.

Increasingly, home became a semi-alien environment for Gerald. His mind was troubled from lack of sleep, as his bed couldn't checker-flag the racetrack in his mind long enough to quell exhaustion. The stark contrast from a space travel research and development whirlwind to the mundane triviality of suburbanville's couch-gazing "What's My Line?" on their black and white television proved untenable to Gerald's questing nature.

Homelife became a paradox of emotional warfare. On one hand, there, to Gerald's delight, dwelt his cherished wife and sons; the jumper cables to his heart's power source of being human. On the other hand, home birthed an unconscious resentfulness by diverting time (however little) and energy away from the shining goal of finding 20th century's Valhalla — that vast aurora-studded celestial hall where dwelt the mysterious, untouched gods of outer space.

Isn't this quest to unmask the greatest and most ancient mystery known to mankind not worthy of any sacrifice? Gerald often asked himself.

Such has been the burning question within many minds seeking nobility of purpose throughout the centuries. As many philosophers and scientists have experienced, the sole focus on anything which continually diverts the eyes from Jesus and his eternal purposes can have depressing consequences. The tragic end result for those who do not re-prioritize is often a soul-sinking, gloomy nihilistic suppressor of the will, where all existence loses meaning.

The Apostle Peter's story in the book of Matthew relates how, after he walked on the surface of the ocean (a "No Technology Required" sign should've been his logo), he began to sink when he looked away from the Lord to behold "the wind boisterous." An understandable diversion, to be sure, but also a life-learning example for those who seek true wisdom.

Gerald's blessing of a great mind — a nearly photographic memory and a proven methodology to apply it — catapulted him to a supervisory position over others at Lockheed with more advanced degrees. Like minds were drawn to him, for as his grandfather often said, "Birds of a feather flock together." While in California, many fellow scientists there were tenured in West Coast universities, not aligned with the Christian family-unity culture of Gerald's roots. Some trivialized spending months at a time away from family as they were immersed in a project or experiment.

Upon re-assignment to NASA in Houston, this lifestyle of abdicating the family role of husband and dad in favor of the all-important quest to conquer space elbowed aside Gerald's traditional love of home and hearth.

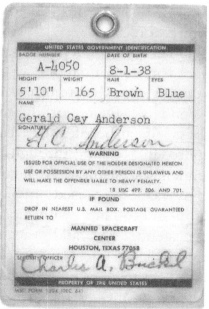

Gerald's NASA security badge.

Subtle at first, but gaining in boldness and destructive momentum in his mind were the challenges from atheistic colleagues in California to Gerald's Christian upbringing. He was worn down by notions that everything in existence bent under the boulder of scientifically exclusive boundaries, defining matter, time, and space while espousing origin by chance. The Christian worldview of supernatural dimensions created by God's design appeared as a weakening Atlas to Gerald after constant exposure to many entrenched nihilistic break-room monologues.

Back in Texas, his family noticed that the dry winds of doubt had drifted east from California alongside Gerald. He disembarked upon Texas soil in possession of an agnostic viewpoint along with the usual baggage. "I'd rather not discuss church or Jesus," Gerald announced to Vida Mae and Sister. Neither elected to question him further on the subject, deciding instead to simply enjoy his long-awaited return home.

Quiet prayers replaced questions. The time wasn't yet right for inquiring more.

Soon after his return to Houston, the family realized Gerald had teetered off the cliff of agnosticism into the near-abyss of disbelief. For years, none were sure how to approach breaking through the crust of Gerald's doubting tendencies without risking alienating him. Any such conversation caused his underbite to become more pronounced and, with nostrils flared, Gerald's oft-used persistence to hold the course on a subject came automatically into play.

All approaches failed to cause a re-birth in Gerald's mind. All except one.

Many considered Gerald to be a modern Renaissance man; self-reliant, well versed in multiple subjects, artistically and scientifically gifted, and confident no horizon could be deemed unreachable. Gerald discovered that one other in the family shared these qualities. Albeit humble in nature (unlike many of the flamboyant intellectuals of Gerald's acquaintance), his grandfather Cay Hughes, from whom Gerald garnered his middle name, possessed a wide array of knowledge and experience. Gerald called him at times to talk about anything and all things.

Papa understood a surprising quantity of scientific facts, Gerald learned. He was an avid reader. The Bible was paramount in Cay's life, but he also subscribed to various scientific journals and sundry periodicals. Papa understood Gerald's quandary about God's un-formulated existence colliding with modern scientific theory. He gently but persuasively reminded Gerald of the many great pioneers of science, such as Isaac Newton, who were convinced the biblical depiction of a Supreme Creator was validated with each scientific revelation. This, along with Papa's first-hand accounts of supernatural works performed by God in his lifetime, began to shake Gerald's post-modern scientific house of straw.

After the conclusion of a successful Gemini project flight and a night of celebratory drinking, which led to a fight with his wife, Gerald found himself in low spirits. As he reached for the phone to contact his Papa for advice, Vida Mae called with the news Papa had passed away. Gerald sat alone on a lawn chair in his garage, chain-smoking cigarettes and stunned by the fact he'd never again hear his grandfather's calming voice of reason.

"Are you up there, Papa?" Gerald asked with features frozen in shock and his moistened eyes peering upward into the deep blue Texas sky. He wished the coming moon shot was re-directed to the uncharted regions of Heaven, and he'd be aboard to locate Papa for one more conversation. He so wanted to be sure of God's existence and, therefore, Papa's heavenly living presence, yet the tendrils of atheism wouldn't free his heart's desire for Christian faith.

Gerald was a man suspended on the swaying tightrope of

life. Could he safely turn around and go back to his family-rooted Christian platform or chance moving on through a building turbulence? Was the other end worth his time, effort, and sacrifice? Or was it a fool's folly as Papa read aloud in days past from Ecclesiastes?

"Papa, are all of man's worldly pursuits only vanity?" Gerald queried the fathomless sky.

He then remembered Papa once insisting that good projects and labors were not useless, as Solomon implied, if man didn't hold these goals above God. "One must be careful," Papa clarified, "that earthly goals do not become an end unto themselves, not even the lofty exploration of space. Such a misplaced priority may have times of high thrills, but the end experience would be emptiness and let-down." Papa expressed in loving tones that God first and foremost created us for His purposes. Our talents must be directed by Him for the true direction and fulfillment of life to be realized.

"Does this require faith in the unseen?" Gerald remembered asking.

"Yes, and you already know this, Gerald. You were raised knowing that we walk by faith. But we can also walk by sight, for our beliefs are proven," Papa asserted. "There's proof of a Creator when one observes the embellishments. There could be a simple existence in most life forms, but God has blessed us with the grandiose. Why does man love and create music and song? Why so many fluctuations of variety and color within species? Why such exacting, intricately complicated physics throughout the living earth that virtually screams intellectual design over mere chance?"

Proof. What Gerald wanted in his present state was hard proof, irrefutable proof, much like a "Doubting Thomas" needing evidence before belief adhered. Looking back, his grandfather's argument for intelligent design provoked a glimmer of... faith?

"Remember, Gerald; we are more than our flesh and blood. As spiritual beings, we have discernment. Yes, we can walk by both faith and sight because the Good Lord has given us the ability to experience Him — His undeniable imprint on this planet and all things on it. Believers see it, but the unbelievers do not. At least, not yet. But the unseeing will be remedied in God's own time, and the resultant light will brighten all perceptions."

True fulfillment and peace of heart define a believer's life, Gerald observed. Papa proved that much.

Recalling these discussions, which played over and over in his head, Gerald began a closer examination of his zeal for future science and space discoveries. He continued to work hard and devote time to NASA. But when man walked on the moon in 1969, Gerald's many celebrations were topped off with a sense of emptiness. The very pursuit of a successful lunar landing, though long and arduous, had been accomplished. The impossible had been achieved, a lifetime ambition fulfilled. A sense of emptiness lurked in its wake.

The achievement itself started a steady decline of ambition within Gerald. Like a dedicated quarterback, the drive downfield proved more exhilarating than the touchdown. Domesticity steadily lost its glow. Perhaps as a side effect of his work vacuum and his estrangement from God, home became a place of awkward silence after the boys went to bed. Both he and Sandra knew the divorce train would soon be on their tracks.

When the Peggy Lee song "Is That All There Is?" was released, Gerald considered it the perfect theme for this stage of life.

***

Unknown to Gerald, his little brother, Johnny, also felt let down but for different reasons. At six foot three and 245 pounds, he'd caught the eye of some college coaches. He and fellow teammate David Hodson were invited to join the Sam Houston State University football team for spring practice his high senior year. They'd leave school after lunch, jump into Johnny's Carmelia blue '68 AMX sports car, and race north on I-45 to Huntsville, where they were suited up and on the field by 2 p.m. Both stayed in the "Animal Dorm" weekends with the starting middle linebacker, senior David Richardson, a great athlete and a well-liked team captain.

Hard work paid off. Both were expected to make the team as "redshirt" freshmen in the fall. They had a blast off the field, finding the college atmosphere enticing as both football and revelry were experienced on a more intense level.

While David was in the proverbial "hog heaven," Johnny had doubts. He wanted to play football at Sam and hang out with the team, but he wasn't sure about attending college. He was tired of school and considered himself a mediocre student. Non-football arguments for college were Gerald and Sister's examples. Both college grads, both well paid because of it. Also, it was Daddy and Mother's dream for Johnny to do likewise.

Reasons for not attending were many. For one thing, he had a girlfriend back home he'd miss. For another thing, he had a girlfriend back home he'd miss! A big reason was one he didn't want to admit — not even to himself.

He was afraid of failure.

All his life, Johnny witnessed the high achievements of Gerald and Sister. Both were scholastic standouts, straight "A" students, and honor society officers with accolades from teachers, coaches, and neighbors on their behalf. Gerald was a Junior Olympic diver and a star gymnast. Sister, brilliant and poised, was voted "Most Beautiful" at school and Gerald "Most Likely to Succeed."

A smiling Johnny graduates with family in attendance. Daddy behind on his left, then Dolly and Gerald. Sister and Mother on his right with nephew Scott and niece Terri in front. Happy day for all!

Johnny often bragged on them. After doing so, folks asked the inevitable: "What happened to you?" This question, though voiced jokingly, stabbed his heart. Johnny

213

felt incriminated for dropping the family banner of exceptionalism. He laughed to cover the pain.

The bar was set impossibly high for little brother. Johnny secretly felt all he did well was to grow big. And strong. He'd inherited the Anderson physical strength and the "Anderson hard-headedness," as Daddy always said. He was good in sports but played for enjoyment, not driven to a professional career as did his buddy David. Unlike Sister and Gerald, Johnny hadn't the foggiest idea of what career path to pursue. This perceived failing weighed heavily upon him.

His reaction in this difficult time of life was to be more reckless in thinking and behavior. Maybe if he were a daredevil, he'd be a standout too.

When he heard that "Victor the Wrestling Bear" would be a side exhibit during an event at Houston's Astrohall, Johnny told his buddies he'd be one of the volunteers to grapple the 450-pound beast. He did so, and friends Weldon Coleman and Billy Hart testified he was the only one of 12 burly contestants Victor didn't defeat. They omitted the fact that Johnny did not wait as instructed for Victor to stand up from pinning the guy before Johnny, but he rushed across the stage and jumped on Victor's back.

Victor's handler, Tuffy Truesdale, whistled the match over after a time as Victor spun in circles with Johnny hanging on for dear life. Then Victor happily waddled over to Tuffy and guzzled a bottle of coke as his reward while Johnny wobbled off in a dizzy state. The audience cracked up.

By Johnny's senior year, he was partying with older athletes. Hanging out with more rowdy cohorts. Indulging in alcohol. It began to affect his easy-going nature. The resultant macho man attitude led to several street fights. He was arrested a few times for such scuffles. Ted worried Johnny was following in his own younger-years errant footsteps.

Upon having to bail his son out of the hoosegow on the night prior to Johnny's Selective Service physical (the Vietnam war was in full swing), Ted knew a serious talk was in order.

Johnny's senior year in High School.

Johnny was charged with inciting a riot for starting a fight with four guys on Main Street in downtown Houston. This time he wasn't even drunk. His buddy, Weldon, recounted that the other teens were stopped next to them at a traffic light. Both vehicles were sports cars with windows rolled down. Random insults were exchanged, and Johnny stunned Weldon and the other guys as he jumped out of Weldon's Camaro, dragged the driver out of his car, and started punching him. When the police arrived, the fight had become a free-for-all.

"That's not like you, son," Ted began with fatherly concern. "I've taught you to fight only when there's a bona fide (he pronounced it 'bone-a-feeday') reason, but this doesn't qualify. And you know it doesn't. What's gotten into you lately? You ain't been acting like yourself."

"I'm sorry, Daddy. Guess I wasn't thinking. It won't happen again," Johnny murmured with his head lowered.

Ted sighed, realizing he wasn't getting anywhere in this vein and lit a cigarette while considering a different approach. "Son, what sort of people did you see locked up in jail?"

"Sir?" Johnny asked, looking up into his daddy's steel-blue, unreadable eyes. Ted repeated the question with no more indication as to intent than he did before. Silence followed.

"Did you see any leaders of the community locked up?" Ted asked with a furrowed brow, like someone pondering a deeply philosophical concept. "Any successful businessmen? Any of your coaches, or doctors, or otherwise respected citizens?"

"No, sir."

"There's a reason for that. Folks who value decency and respect don't give themselves over to the kind of behavior that results in jail time. Nor do they associate with others who do. You'll have to make up your mind about what kind of man you're going to be. It's your choice. If you like what you saw in jail, then keep on the way you're going. But if you choose to honor the good name of our family and the ways of your upbringing, then make changes. The first change is to stop hanging out with some of the people who're leading you down the wrong path."

"Daddy, I want to make ya'll proud of me," Johnny avowed sincerely. "I just messed up, and it wasn't Weldon's fault."

"I didn't say it was, son. And I'm not implying him. But you know the so-called friends I'm referring to. At Zestos, we hear a lot of what goes on behind the scenes in our neighborhood, so don't think anybody can pull the wool over our eyes. I'm a good judge of character, and I hope you'll see the truth behind the mask some folks wear. The Lord gave you a lot of talents and abilities. Use them for good and stop peeing them to the four winds."

"All right, Dad — "

Ted cut him off. "Don't expect to make a change for the better until you change company," he stated emphatically, tossing the cigarette onto the garage floor and stomping it out with his shoe.

"Mother's worried, too. She wants what's best for you, and the notion that you could be drafted into the Vietnam War has her on pins and needles. She and Sister are praying for you night and day, son."

Johnny, looking thoughtful, said, "I know that's right. Mother tells me she prays I won't get drafted because I'm too big a target."

Ted started to say something but stopped himself. He was worried about that, too. He couldn't bear the thought of Johnny dying in war. He looked with disdain at the crushed stub of his cigarette, saying, "Johnny, don't you ever smoke the first one of these coffin nails. These dang things are gonna kill me someday!" He angrily stood up, then turned to say, "I almost forgot; your Uncle Jimmy wants you to call him. Tell him hello for me when you do."

***

After a few minutes of small talk, Jimmy Brent admitted he'd heard of Johnny's troubles. Johnny related the points Ted made about keeping bad company.

"I don't think others have such a strong influence on me, Uncle Jimmy. Some things those friends do, I'd never do. After all, I'm not a kid anymore," Johnny said defensively.

"Age doesn't lessen the effect of friends on our ways of thinking, Johnny," Uncle Jimmy responded. "We all tend to act much like our associates. Over time, our perceptions line up with theirs." When Johnny didn't reply, he counseled, "In the old days of cowboy trail drives, they used a lead steer out front to guide the herd in dangerous territory. A lead steer is experienced on the trail, familiar with low-water crossings and unstable paths. The other cows follow him. This steer was never sold at market like the others but returned to the ranch where he was pampered until the next season's drive. He was highly valued because of his worth as a good leader. Cowboys lost less cattle along the trail with a seasoned and trusted lead steer out front."

Uncle Jimmy paused to let his words sink in.

"Another kind of leader steer was used for a different purpose. This one led other cows to the slaughterhouse chutes. One didn't need a bunch of ranch hands to keep the cattle moving through the pens with this steer in action. He was spared to lead again and was never butchered. This kind was known as the 'Judas Steer' after the traitor in the Bible."

"I'm not a..." Johnny began to protest, but Uncle Jimmy

interrupted.

"I know you're not a cow, Johnny. But our instincts aren't too different when it comes to following others. Unlike cows, we are blessed with the intellect to use the discernment God gives us to choose good associations. Else we chance coming to a bad end behind a Judas."

This, of course, caused Johnny to recall the exact same word his grandfather Cay had shared — discernment.

Jimmy finished with, "It's tough to sever friendships, but sometimes it must be done. I know you'll do the right thing, Johnny."

The next few years were a blur to Johnny. He married his long-time girlfriend on a quick decision, and they had a baby son within the year. Jeffrey Anderson was the one bright spot for them both in a marriage that never really got off the ground relationally. While dating, their many differences didn't distract from their love affair. Short-term exposures to one another were easy. Marriage proved another story, and the friction that developed made life unbearable.

Just before Jeffrey was born, Johnny got a job working long, hard hours as a millwright helper in a local paper mill. They'd moved in temporarily with Ted and Vida Mae so Johnny's wife wouldn't be alone in the final stages of pregnancy. On New Year's Eve morning, as Johnny left for work, Vida Mae pleaded for him to stay home, as she'd a terrible premonition of danger. He assured her he'd work safe and would be fine. They needed the job and the overtime money it paid.

After a grueling 14 hours at work, Johnny was driving home on Old Highway 90 when a speeding pair of headlights in the oncoming lane drifted across the yellow stripes, racing straight for him. Numb from fatigue, Johnny hesitated before braking hard in response and steered toward the pavement's right, desperate to avoid a collision. The headlights were tilted slightly up on the oncoming vehicle, indicating the accelerator was floor-boarded.

Little Jeff pets "Sam", puppy belonging to Vida Mae's good neighbors, the Lindeens.

The distance quickly closed between them, and Johnny felt a cold, unnaturally calm dread of the upcoming wreck that would probably kill both drivers. There was nothing he could do to prevent disaster. Past the road's right shoulder was a large bar ditch, at least six feet deep and ten feet wide. To the left was the oncoming traffic lane.

Johnny's size and strength were useless to him now. He was trapped and powerless.

Thirty feet before the vehicles collided, the oncoming Buick Riviera veered sharply left, missing Johnny by mere feet. Bucking dramatically upward upon striking the slight rise of the shoulder, it then nose-dived into the bar ditch with a cascade of flying dirt, dust, and shale. The pavement shuddered under Johnny's car as the Buick slammed into a large embedded concrete culvert. A geyser of glass and chrome shot upward like a July 4th fireworks display. Johnny stopped his vehicle and jumped out, running to the crumpled, smoking Buick.

A cacophony of sounds emitted from the Buick. The radio blared Hank Williams' "Your Cheatin' Heart" as the auto's damaged horn whined like some hellish organ, adding a weird dimension to the mangled wreckage. Looking into the open driver's window, Johnny beheld an unconscious, overweight, 30-ish man bleeding profusely from a cracked skull and breathing ragged, uneven gulps of air. Bloody bubbles encrusted his lips.

Strong odors of urine and alcohol mixed with burning electrical wires drew Johnny's widened eyes to the beer can-littered floorboard. The blue jean inseams of both pant legs were split open to the urine-stained crotch, a result of the driver's legs absorbing a tremendous shock wave from the impact. The putrid air evidenced that the bowels and bladder had released.

A family group photo, fixed onto the sun visor, now dangled before the driver's closed eyes. One last belabored breath exhaled slowly from the dying man's bloody lips, sounding like a whispered "No."

A gold wedding ring gleamed on the driver's left hand. Someone's husband, someone's dad, someone's son would not come home tonight. "Happy New Year," Johnny breathed sorrowfully in irony of the now-tragic holiday while driving away from death's hideous workmanship.

He'd have another tomorrow, unstolen, undenied. This wasn't the case for the Buick's driver.

Taking his wedding ring out of his pocket where it stayed during work, he slipped it over a dirty left finger. Should he crash and burn before arriving home, Johnny wanted it known he was a family man. Although a poor example of a husband in his own mind, there was some honor in this.

Why was I spared? he pondered all week and for many to come. The question changed forms during the decade to include searching for purpose. He figured Mother's prayers played a part in his escape, but a suitable answer remained elusive. A mysterious veil was drawn across the hallway to Johnny's future, and that veil was about to become darker.

***

"Stage 2 lung cancer is the diagnosis," Vida Mae relayed to Sister in a quivering voice. "Surgery to remove your daddy's right lung is scheduled the day after Johnny's 24th birthday."

"Oh, Mother, let's pray!" Sister exclaimed as her heart yearned to join Mother's in seeking God's peace and guidance. Mother nodded tearfully. They joined hands and knelt together in Vida Mae's living room. Sunbeams streaked through large sectioned windows as they prayed, showcasing the backyard live oak tree and its surrounding bed of colorful day lilies. Troubled prayers arose through tranquil scenery.

Their prayers transcended Ted's diagnosis. Without restraint, both bared heart and soul before God Almighty. Mercy was needed for much more than a physical healing. The specter of spiritual deaths threatening Gerald and Johnny spurred the women to pray with an urgency equal to that of Ted's physical danger. Vida Mae and Sister beseeched God for a spiritual awakening, a deliverance from the tumors of deception and misguidance darkening the portals of eternity in Gerald and Johnny's lives.

The younger brother believed in God but doubted he could live a Christian's life. The elder thought science denied God's existence while yearning, somehow, to be proven wrong. Both admired their daddy, and without his stabilizing influence, the slow-yet-steady rescue of the boys might well be aborted.

Divorce looked to be a certainty in both marriages. Gerald no longer lived at home with Sandra. He only phoned occasionally, confiding in Ted alone of deeply personal issues. Consequently, he was drinking more, and he made no efforts to hide it. He loved Mother and Sister but seemed unable to open up the deepest areas of his heart to them. Gerald brushed off their attempts to understand his innermost struggles with declarations he didn't wish to cause them worry.

The on-again, off-again marriage between Johnny and his wife, Dolly, worried the rest of the family. He, too, spoke bluntly about personal issues, sharing details only with Ted. Vida Mae overheard enough to know Johnny was greatly troubled, but it was instinct that gave her the most uneasiness. Mother sensed her son was spiritually desperate. She felt he wanted to make changes in his life and reconcile with Dolly but didn't know how to do so without surrendering his individuality. He didn't recognize his individuality as being composed of false pride.

Vida Mae and Sister prayed for Ted to survive surgery and for a change of direction in his sons. Without him, they envisioned both brothers edging farther away from the Lord. But for now, Ted was making some headway with his sons. He spoke a man's language and brought the Good Lord's name up whenever he felt the time was right. Gerald and Johnny related to their daddy and listened to him.

Should cancer take Ted out of the family, his influence would be irreplaceable. Doctors made it clear that such drastic surgery meant odds were even he'd never get off the operating table. Ted's absence would create a painful void in their hearts and lives. They couldn't bear to consider it.

Reverend Joe Granberry met with Ted before the operation and prayed privately with him. Vida Mae and Ted's kids spent a final few minutes by his side until he was wheeled into surgery. After four hours, doctors emerged to inform the family Ted was expected to live, and they felt like all of the tumor was removed. Chemotherapy was scheduled for weeks afterward.

Vida Mae with a big Loggerhead Snapping turtle. She'd snagged him before while fishing, but he escaped. Ted didn't believe her story of his size, joking to Zestos customers they were afraid to fish Horse Pen Creek because 'A dinosaur keeps us run off!' Vida Mae had the last laugh a year later, hauling in this 48-pound behemoth.

The next few months were good times in the memories of the family. Ted seemed like a new man. Though weak from chemotherapy, he relished life more, often laughing at things he used to curse and no longer regarding Zestos as the master of his time. Already having closed the store

Mondays for day trips to the "country," he began to open later and close earlier.

Left to Right: Matie, Vita Mae, Elsie & Madelene cooking over a big pioneer skillet in the 'country'.

Ted's relationship with his youngest son became stronger. Johnny developed new insight into his daddy's reasons for actions that used to be baffling. One day while at the camp, Ted was admonishing Johnny for not renewing efforts to make peace with his estranged wife.

"Johnny, a man that won't at least try to make up with his wife is missing the boat. Marriage and raising a family is good for a man. Keep this up, and one day you'll wind up useless as teats on a boar hog!" Instead of feeling resentment that once resulted from such words, Johnny understood this was Daddy's unique way of expressing concern, fatherly direction, and love.

He smiled at the good intention behind the crude phrase,

and with a big grin, lightly quipped, "Maybe so, Daddy, but I'm cute anyway, ain't I?"

Ted turned quickly around from where he was working on their old John Deere tractor. The surprised look on his face made Johnny laugh out loud. After a moment, Ted's face relaxed, and he tilted his head back as one of his extra-noisy belly laughs burst forth, ringing throughout the pine treetops and across the green hillsides, causing a nearby fox squirrel to chatter in alarm.

Johnny never again heard such statements from his daddy. In Ted's mind, his son had matured into manhood. He would now be addressed differently. Both sensed this milestone.

The third week of November 1974, Ted and Vida Mae were in the camp, having closed the store for the week to celebrate Thanksgiving. Ted was in good spirits, excitedly planning activities in anticipation of Johnny's arrival the following morning. Father and son had grown very close since Ted's surgery. Johnny took a week's vacation from his job in order to do chores around camp for Ted, who was still recovering from his bout with cancer.

Reminiscing about the sweet news they were expecting a baby twenty-five years ago, Ted's love for his little boy-now-grown man escalated into an unquenchable urge to bear-hug Johnny the moment he wheeled into camp.

He never got to see his son again, nor give that loving hug.

Later that night, Ted began to cough uncontrollably, escalating to the point his breathing was strangled. They loaded into his Ford truck and rushed to the hospital in Woodville. Ted insisted on driving the three miles from camp to Highway 190, for the dirt roads were slick from recent rains, and he couldn't chance getting stuck.

Ted in his beloved 'Country' camp, cooking for family in 1974.

If they did and couldn't get to the hospital in time, Ted didn't want this to put a burden of guilt on his sweet wife. He'd protected her for 40 years and would continue to do so at all costs.

With great effort, Ted made the blacktop highway before passing out. Vida Mae moved him aside on the truck's bench seat and sped the remaining ten miles to the emergency room. It was the longest ten miles of her life. She was on the same road traveled by her Papa 66 years earlier, with Momma near death in their farm wagon. Vida Mae often wondered how Papa felt on that desperate, prayer-paved journey. Now she knew.

Doctors wouldn't let her into the treatment room, but she peeked through the door when a nurse rushed out. She caught a glimpse of Ted on a table, under an oxygen tent, eyes wide open and peering curiously around the room. She relaxed, thinking he'd be okay.

One hour later, Vida Mae was informed that Ted Anderson, her husband of 40 years, was gone.

Sinking to her knees in the lonely, sanitized-smelling waiting room, she instinctively sought sanctuary in the Good Lord. While praying for mercy and strength, memories swirled through the rising swells of pain, causing a hodgepodge of mental scenes and words from years past to flutter erratically, like butterflies in a violent storm through Vida Mae's anguished mind.

Handsome young Ted's overconfident expression as he sidled into church next to her 41 years ago flashed before her. She could almost smell the ridiculous combination of Old Spice cologne and rye whiskey from that sunny, semi-disastrous day. Her heart diverted momentarily from the intense emptiness as she relived the moment his charms turned her anger into a hope-filled wonder.

Unlikely as it seemed then, it was during that long-ago moment Vida Mae fell in love.

Days later, while standing by Ted's casket, it occurred to her that God, in His infinite mercy, could've halted the love between a man and a woman when one died. Maybe like when a cruel hand pulls the tail off a lizard, yet the lizard easily grows another tail, thus becoming whole again. Yet, Vida Mae thought, *God lets the human heart continue to twitch and hurt, as the forlorn, incomplete survivor yearns for healing.* She wondered why this was so.

A distinct voice in her head told her that true love is too powerful to end when one heart stops beating. Also, there's a season for all things, for the finite earth and all upon it are created to undergo change. A season to laugh and rejoice, a season to mourn and lament, and a season to grow through trials into a person of great faith.

And people of great faith are never without hope. Momma and Papa proved that.

Loving hearts are made complete by peace in the living God who has defeated death and never abandons nor forsakes His children. Not in seasons of plenty, nor in drought.

The words of John 14:27 entered into Vida Mae's mind, "Peace I leave with you, my peace I give to you: not as the world gives, give I unto you. Let not your heart be troubled, neither let it be afraid." Then a new train of thought reminded her that God's mercy was evident all through their marriage. By rights, Ted should have died 30 years ago from his awful fall; or at the very least been terribly crippled. By rights, Vida Mae should've died in the Butane explosion. By rights, Norma Jean and Gerald should have been orphaned; and Johnny never born.

Yes, God showered them with mercy and blessings for years. She vowed to remember these things and trust Him.

Immediately, an unexplainable peace began to relieve Vida Mae, settling and strengthening her spirit through the pain. This verse became her favorite for all her life.

During Ted's funeral, Vida Mae overheard Sister express thankfulness to God that Daddy didn't suffer for months in a cold hospital room, but died in the place he loved the most, doing what he loved most, and was with the one he loved most.

Ted on his John Deere tractor with Vida Mae, Sandra, and Gerald's boys, Steve and David.

These words comforted Vida Mae and caused her to reflect on how seldom she and Ted had outwardly professed their love one to another. Some couples constantly said, "I love you" to each other. Neither she nor Ted ever doubted the other's love. Though it was unspoken, both were secure of this at all times. Her heart warmed as she remembered the first time they'd exchanged declarations of love. Their marriage soon followed. Her heart swelled with the desire to say it one last time.

"I love you, Ted Anderson." She smiled sweetly at the still face. It was a tearful goodbye, but without the ominous dread of the previous few days. The Lord's touch of comfort brought a new season forth in her heart and gradually ushered out the old season's ending with an order and tenderness that her soul began to understand.

Though tragic for the moment, everything taking place was the will of a good and loving God.

Later, Vida Mae observed her sons and daughter together in earnest conversation, and she thought Sister might be counseling them about marriage. She'd noticed the distanced attitude lately between both sons and their wives. Their alienation was obvious and forebode that, unless something extraordinary happened, both couples would divorce.

Little did she know, Johnny's wife had just informed him she'd filed for divorce. Her reason for the bad timing was tied to Ted's demise. He'd spoken often to them about forgiving and reuniting. With him gone, saving their marriage was a lost cause. Johnny understood and chose not to blame her for divorcing now. He knew he had not been a good husband.

"Mother," Sister began gently, "Your employees asked if you're accepting one of the many offers to buy Zestos. We've told them to wait for you to consider the best offer. Some are anxious to know if they should start a new job search. I took the liberty to inform them it's a good bet you'll sell. We can't visualize how you could possibly run the business by yourself. It took all the time and effort from you and Daddy both to operate the store, rising early six days a week. You worked past closing at 9 p.m. with only short mid-day breaks. It's too much for one person."

Gerald and Johnny opened their mouths to speak at the same time, but Vida Mae stopped them, reaching out and placing a hand on their arms. "Before y'all chime in with Sister about this, I need to pray about it. I love you very much and value your thoughts about what to do. Selling does make sense. But I need the Lord to direct our decisions, just like when we first opened the store. God knows what's best."

The following morning, Vida Mae arose early and made

coffee —she'd habitually made enough for her and Ted, just like always — then made some calls before going shopping. She bought "thank you" cards to send out to relatives and friends for attending the funeral and one extra purchase of a small sign. Upon meeting her children at Zestos, she calmly asked all three to sit down while she explained her decision.

"After much prayer, I'm reopening Zestos. Your daddy and I shared some big dreams about this store and the contributions to this community resulting from it. We've formed a special bond with many fine folks through this business, and I believe the Lord's not finished with the Anderson's Zestos yet."

No one said a word, although their eyes widened with surprise.

"Ted's absence will create a vacuum, of course. He had such a way with kids! They're going to miss his good-natured teasing and big laugh...so will we all." Vida Mae hesitated as a catch in her throat watered her eyes. Sister put her hand to her own heart in a feminine gesture of compassion, then gave Mother a quick hug of encouragement.

"But if Ted were here now, he'd agree and would be the first to turn that "closed" sign around. To him, a permanent close is the same as quitting. As he often said, "Can't and Quit ain't in my dictionary!" as I'm sure y'all recall." Vida Mae smiled.

"So, I've done three things this morning. First, I called our employees and told them to be ready to work at their usual times the day after tomorrow. Second, I called our suppliers, including White Swan, for resupply of drink cups and Mims Meat for fresh hamburger patties to be delivered Tuesday morning."

Vida Mae looked at her small audience of family members and soaked in their smiles. "Lastly, I bought this little wall sign. Gerald, would you hang this up over my desk, please?"

Gerald removed the packing paper from the 12" x 12" framed sign, revealing the words:

AIN'T NOTHIN' GONNA COME UP TODAY THAT ME AND THE LORD CAN'T HANDLE.

Gerald looked at Johnny and saw his little brother's eyes shining with pride. He understood. He felt his own underbite thrust out in the Anderson family's history of resolute determination to overcome any obstacle. Sister's eyes glistened as well, not from remorse of Daddy's death, but of something else. Something of high value that's difficult to express in human words, but nevertheless crystal clear in her magnificent heart.

It occurred to her that Daddy's saying that "quit" or "can't" wasn't in his dictionary DID put into words the little sign's creed, adding the vital element of a trust in God to gel this winning attitude.

"That sign will be my motto for the days ahead. I'm sure things will work out okay," Vida Mae avowed calmly and confidently. Thinking of what Ted would say if he were present, she quipped, "Besides, we've got customers that eat here every day without fail. If Zestos closed, they'd starve plumb to death!"

All four erupted into laughter. Johnny sank to his knees, holding his middle in the most robust belly laugh he'd had in weeks. Wiping tears of mirth away and straightening her dress, Vida Mae reflected that somewhere, Ted was laughing too, and God was probably smiling down on the healing taking place in a small ice cream store.

That night, Johnny and his ex-teammate, David, went to a nightclub across the ship channel. Johnny had troubling thoughts mixed with regret about Ted's passing. He felt he'd not lived up to his daddy's expectations, nor his own. He should've graduated college by now, like Sister and Gerald. Yet, he still had no ideas for a career path. Plus, he'd be the first in the family to divorce, a significant failure.

On multiple occasions, the question of why God saved him from serious injury or death revisited him, as Daddy's unexpected death brought a harsh reality to the subject.

What, if anything, is God trying to tell me? rambled through his mind. Praying at Daddy's funeral, he felt something else was in store soon. But what? When? It was as if the whole world was on a set course except him, and he was stuck in neutral.

Going to a club, having a few drinks, and forgetting the mental quicksand awhile seemed a way to relieve his mind of these infernal questions. After midnight, he and David left the club, and Johnny's car overheated on Federal Road, two miles from home. They began to walk but encountered a long, slow-moving freight train blocking their path. Feeling adventurous, Johnny began to run down the tracks opposite the train's forward travel, then jumped onto a boxcar, calling for David to follow.

"Johnny, are you crazy?" David shouted, following Johnny's example. Climbing sideways around the front of the boxcar, Johnny stepped over the coupling that attached the car to the one before it, coming out on the other side of the train. They could jump onto the street as the train approached it and be on their way. He perched on the bottom rung that formed a side-ladder, used by brakemen to climb on top of the boxcar. The ladder's rung was a simple steel rebar, formed like a U, and welded onto the boxcar frame.

As the train came abreast of the Federal Road crossing, Johnny hollered back to David, "Jump after I do!" With that, he launched himself off his right foot, intending to land and roll onto the road. As he'd leaped forward and outward, Johnny felt someone grab his right foot, anchoring it to the ladder rung.

With a panicked jolt, he felt his body's momentum check short and begin to plunge downward where the train's solid-steel wheels clicked and clattered in the quiet night like a mechanical, soul-less leviathan across the undulating iron rails. He realized in that fraction of a moment that death awaited him a mere four feet down. He'd swing like a living pendulum by his fixed right foot until the flesh and bones of his shoulders and head were pulverized by those powerfully grinding wheels.

The shock barely struck his inebriated mind with the full horror of a mangling death by train when his foot released. He crashed on both elbows onto the concrete road surface. David landed ten feet farther down the tracks onto the road's shoulder.

Just before Johnny hit the pavement, the shock of it all was interrupted by an oddly random assurance he'd not be harmed tonight. An untold destiny awaited him. The source and cause were a fleeting mystery. Things were happening too fast to ponder it now.

Springing up, David rushed over to Johnny, who was sitting upright a mere two feet from the rambling freight train, examining his bleeding elbows. "David, you idiot!" he shouted over the train's racket. "Why did you grab my foot?!"

"I didn't grab you! But I saw you stop in the middle of the jump," David countered. "Scoot back! You're too dadgum close to the train!"

Rising slowly, Johnny hobbled on one side severely. Looking at his right foot, he saw one boot heel was missing. Pulling the boot off and turning it upside down, he was perplexed to see only nail ends protruding where a two-inch heel once was.

It then dawned on him what had happened. The heel was

forced down and wedged fast between the rebar step and the wall of the boxcar. When Johnny launched himself upward, it stuck fast before breaking off. They searched the road where he'd landed in vain for the missing boot heel.

David and Johnny looked at each other in amazement as both realized the boot heel was still stuck in the rebar, riding its solitary journey to the train's destination. Johnny had the quirky vision of a bewildered brakeman's squinting face upon discovering a boot heel passenger on the boxcar.

Try as they might, neither strong young man could break off the remaining heel so Johnny could walk evenly. He removed both boots and walked in his socks. Both friends sauntered along in shocked silence. Johnny, now fully sober, thanked God with every stride.

Somewhere in the distance, the train whistle blew, sounding forlorn and suppressed by the humid night air, as if robbed of its chance for infamy. After a time, David stopped walking, turned to Johnny, and spoke soberly, reverently. "That scared me to death, Johnny. Somebody up there's watching over you."

Johnny recalled another football teammate, Alan, saying those same words to him on the night of his 21st birthday. They'd celebrated at various nightclubs on McCarty Drive, a rowdy area of beer joints frequented by sailors fresh off the nearby docks. Johnny reacted forcefully to a drunken challenger of a billiard game before the two friends left at midnight for another club. A few blocks down the road, a car followed them closely, with bright lights flickering on and off.

Thinking it was the pool game adversary, Johnny pulled over to accommodate a more emphatic ending to the dispute. While opening his door, a crazy-eyed, wild-haired smallish man jumped from his car with a shouldered Browning semi-auto shotgun leveled with hostile intent.

Johnny swung his legs back inside and slowly shut the driver's door of his AMX, his belligerence replaced with the extreme pucker-factor effect of a 12-gauge shotgun. The crazy stranger, who looked like the recently publicized California killer, Charles Manson, rushed to Johnny's open window. With a string of drug-induced expletives, he aimed the barrel two feet from Johnny's face.

An audible click signified the gun's safety was off. He furiously spewed the run-together words, "You messed with the Starlite Inn! I'm gonna blow yer head off!"

Hearing a faint moan of dread from Alan, Johnny didn't look away or flinch. His gut told him to look calm and speak slowly, for just as a person can sense the moment a dog's about to bite or a man's going to throw a punch, this guy was about to pull the trigger. Johnny had a flash vision of his poor mother weeping by the grave of her young son, who never amounted to much and was killed senselessly on McCarty Drive.

Just then, a small message, not really a voice or thought, stirred in Johnny's heart. It was a timely reassurance, a revelation that his time had not yet come.

"Sorry, amigo, but you have the wrong guy," Johnny said softly with all the steadiness he could muster. "We haven't harmed the Starlite. My friend and I are going to Big Roy's Cafe for a bite, that's all. Not looking for any trouble. I pulled over 'cause I thought your car broke down and figured to give you a hand."

The urge to shoot flashed on and off in Crazy Charlie's eyes, and he abruptly lowered the barrel and blasted the ground directly under Johnny's car seat. He quickly jerked the barrel back up into Johnny's face. It looked like the business end of a cannon. The acrid smell of burnt cordite from the discharged shell wafted out of the gun barrel and into the AMX.

Alan moaned louder.

More terse seconds passed as conflicting impulses cycled again in Crazy Charlie's eyes before he stepped back two paces, lowering the shotgun slightly. Johnny nodded in understanding. Striving to avoid a case of 12-gauge-itis, he drove slowly away like a decrepit grandpa leaving church.

Crazy Charlie's electric stare followed them like the clinging stench of a road-killed skunk.

WED. SEPT. 1, 1965

Chronicle Photo by Orie Collins

When the Furr High Freshmen tangle with the Spring Branch Frosh Thursday at 3 p.m. at Furr field, 500 Mercury, these three boys will do heavy line duty for Furr. The freshmen play at the same time as the Furr varsity which takes on Ross Sterling High in a pre-season scrimmage at an adjacent arena. Left to right: David Hodson, 15, 4835 O.S.T., right tackle; Allen Sciba, 15, 10605 Duncum, right guard, and Johnny Anderson, 15, 10218 Fleming, left tackle.

School football article with photo, published in the Houston Chronicle showing Johnny (far r.) with friends and teammates Alan Sciba (middle) and David Hodson. 1965.

"I, I don't know how we got outta that one," Alan stuttered nervously. "He wanted to kill you. And me too, probably. Man, oh man! Somebody up there is watching over you."

Alan declined to hang out much with Johnny after that night. Years later, after the freight train incident, David also showed some reluctance to go out on the town with his buddy. It brought to mind the lead steer stories told by Uncle Jimmy... and Johnny felt the blush of shame that he had nearly been the "Judas"-type steer that led his friends into mortal danger.

Yet apparently, the Good Lord still honored Mother's covering prayers, and He did have a destiny for her son. Johnny had not a clue as to what that might be. He felt unworthy of any good future.

***

Both Johnny and Gerald divorced within a few years. Gerald eventually paired with a lady friend who bent the elbow daily and didn't ask questions. Johnny hardened his heart against falling in love again, vowing only to date and never marry. His ex-wife remarried and moved to New Mexico, taking little Jeffrey with her.

Sister and Walter did well, each starting their own business. Both Terri and Scott shone academically and were happily active in church.

Sister's faithfulness to God never wavered. Johnny and Gerald loved and admired her, as did all who came in contact with Norma Jean. Her CPA business flourished as her reputation for honesty and diligence spread.

Soon after burying her husband, Vida Mae had an interesting encounter. One punk in the area decided that Zestos would be an easy mark to score some extra cash with Ted gone. He waited until just before closing on a Friday night. As the last customer drove off, he sidled up to the store and reached down to pull up his sagging britches.

Vida Mae serving a customer at Zestos window.

Jerking a long-barreled revolver from his waistband, he thrust the barrel menacingly through the open window. Before his scrunched face could utter a demand, Vida Mae reached forward and, with a sweep of the left hand, brushed the gun barrel aside, saying sternly, "Oh, get that thing outta here!"

Shocked at her unexpected response, he paused with mouth open and britches sagging to watch incredulously as Vida Mae calmly closed and locked the window. With one last defeated glance at five-foot two-inch Vida Mae, armed with nothing but a pink, grease-stained apron, the frustrated felon dashed away into the consoling night. Surprised at her own brazen reactions upon later reflection, Vida Mae sat in her office staring at the little sign on the wall, giving copious thanks to the Lord.

Ted and his tough-guy reputation may be gone, but Mrs. Anderson proved well able to hold the fort on her own.

Vida Mae did have help from her children from time to time. She began to close Zestos two days a week, taking off Sundays (along with Monday) to attend church. Contrary to Ted's assertions that doing so would harm their business, Vida Mae discovered her customers didn't abandon them to frequent other eateries but waited until Tuesday to flock en masse back to the store. Apart from some grumbling over two whole days without Zestos fare, they were always happy to see her open for business and that famous smile welcoming them back.

To everyone's amazement, including her own, she ran Zestos very successfully for another 17 years after Ted's passing, saving numerous customers from starving to death.

Chapter Eight: Just Love 'Em

"I'm gonna shoot your son if he don't start talking!" the slurred voice rasped from the phone before Vida Mae could say hello. The luminescent digital clock next to her bed glowed 2:45 a.m.

All she could think to say was, "Come again?"

Clattering sounds, muffled voices, and a small dog's barking were the only reply.

"I'm sorry, Mother, "Gerald's reassuring voice came on moments later, stemming her rising anxiety. "We were having an argument. She got mad when I tired of fussing and clammed up. Didn't know she'd call you. Go back to sleep, and I'll call you tomorrow. Good night."

Vida Mae laid back onto her pillow, her worried brow's furrows dimly reflected in the greenish glow of the small clock. Off in the distance, a lonely siren whined from an emergency vehicle racing down Interstate Highway 10, harmonizing with the alarm in her mother's heart.

Excepting business ventures, the decade of the '80s started off unkind to Gerald. He'd left the Aerospace industry, becoming a consultant in everything computers for a variety of businesses. Gerald gained a reputation for efficiency and innovation. By 1985 he had a waiting list of clients that needed source programs written with software or hardware troubleshooting performed. The money was good.

In his private life, things got hairy. Being a brainiac, he discovered a few drinks helped him fit in more effortlessly among others in the local single-scene. Alcohol called the shots, and for the first time in his life, Gerald encountered something he couldn't master. Social drinking had morphed behind the scenes from a friendly hobby into a full-time demanding mistress. His new lady friend increased her intake, too. Beer ushered in hard liquor, and the couple's friends noticed a disturbing difference in her inebriated personality. The jovial lady who laughed and talked freely between sips of suds retreated inside herself on hard liquor to a darkened place as the bottle level fell.

Invitations to parties and social gatherings dwindled as her usual empathy towards others transformed to unprovoked hostility as the night wore on. Gerald found this down-stepping change hard to deal with. His efforts to get her off a tirade by changing subjects during hostilities only invoked harsher responses. They both became argumentative, resulting in long silences at home as an escape from insults. Daily life was bearable to Gerald while working, but the nights and weekends were like strolling through a haunted house.

Surprises were never good, and no peace was to be found.

Across town, Johnny was finishing his three-mile morning jog and thinking about his brother. Vida Mae had called before his workout and was very upset, asking Johnny to pray for Gerald's safety. The promised follow-up call had come from Gerald that next morning after the threat. He tried to reassure Mother, saying they'd worked things out and he was in no danger.

"My intuition is not convinced!" Vida Mae declared as she notified Sister and Johnny to stay in prayer. Little brother was praying more the last few years about a lot of subjects. Life for Johnny stabilized from the crazy-party years after Ted's demise, and though he still drank, it wasn't frequently. He dieted, losing the 50 pounds he'd gained since high school, got back in good physical condition, and worked with a construction company as a purchasing agent. He bought a small house in North Shore.

One year after that scary phone call, a horrible event indicated their prayers were heard. Threats were tragically acted upon, but Gerald was spared. In a moment of drunken frustration, his lady friend pulled the trigger, firing one shot that ended her life.

This senseless tragedy combined with serious health issues brought Gerald to a point of decision. While agonizing over her death, he knew drastic changes must be made before he could disembark from the destructive merry-go-round of late. Alcohol, once seen as an escape from the mental captivity of his all-work-and-no-play mind, now revealed itself as a slave master in disguise. Gerald concluded that life's escapees who sought safe harbor in the bottle's much-publicized revelry eventually find the party lights dimming until there was no way out of total darkness. He knew that either the party or his life would soon end.

Addiction darkness starts first as spiritual deception by distancing from God, then deteriorates emotionally with spasmodic mood crashes, eroding that which is relational by the snake bite of distrust towards those who give genuine love. If no intervention, it kills the physical being.

After emergency surgery to save his pancreas, Gerald, at last, heeded the advice of his doctors and family. He wanted to live to the fullest and make life count for something worthwhile again.

His last carton of cigarettes was given to an ornery neighbor. He poured alcohol down the kitchen sink, and the gurgling prompted him to hum the 1965 song "Bye Bye Baby, Goodbye." The empty bottles were cast into the garbage with an overhand flourish like Magic Johnson slam-dunking a basketball.

Gerald returned to his roots as he healed, spending time with family and trusted friends and reading classic literature like Melville's *Moby Dick*. As he marveled in the similarity of Melville's Captain Ahab and Gerald's common obsession with their pursuit of an other-worldly goal, one a great mystical white whale, the other a vast universe of planetary question marks, the phone rang.

"Hey, Gerald, tomorrow's Mother's Day, and Sister asked if you want to meet us at church, with dinner afterward," Johnny asked. Gerald paused in thought while stroking his mustache and goatee. He'd grown the beard to help disguise his pronounced underbite but had come to like the effect on his general appearance. He looked more studious now.

"Let me think about it, Johnny. I'd kind of like to sleep in tomorrow, but will meet y'all for lunch if not at church. I'll call you back later with my decision."

Within the hour, Gerald became drowsy while reading, eventually dozing off into a deep sleep. He began to dream, envisioning a huge white fin breaking the surface of a turbulent ocean. Leaning over the side of the boat to peer closer into the water, he saw a horribly disfigured face rise from the murky depths, the pale lips forming his name. Jolting awake, the book tumbled to the floor, and Gerald reached instinctively for the usual glass of vodka on the coffee table. Nothing was there. Reality flooded back as the dream faded, but Gerald sensed his resolve to change and stay sober being challenged by an unseen adversary. He decided going to church for the first time in years would be a good start in resisting this challenge. And spending the morrow with cherished family was a fine idea. He called Johnny back.

Greens Bayou Assembly bustled inside the sanctuary, with families selecting seats for extra visitors. Outside, old friends exiting their cars reunited with shouts of recognition, hugging robustly in the graveled parking lot before service, as the morning sun shone in bright splendor from an indigo blue sky. To the surprise of the Andersons, Vida Mae's uncle Jerry Harrison emerged from Matie's sedan, bent over from age and hair silvery-white. As Gerald walked quickly to the sedan to help place his walking cane steadily under him, Uncle Jerry recognized his great-nephew.

"Why, Gerald Cay!!" he exclaimed with gusto and a thrilled expression so bursting with delight that Johnny's mind held the image vividly for all his days. The great love in Uncle Jerry's heart was on such stirring display that everyone in the parking lot later asked Vida Mae for the name and story of that precious old gentleman.

After church, Uncle Jerry, in his nineties and the last surviving Harrison brother, told of George Harrison's funeral months earlier and the legacy he'd left with the church.

"Overhearing some in your congregation," he began in a slightly-trembled voice, "spreading rumors your preacher may leave soon, brought to mind George's last sermon. After 70 years of preaching the Gospel, his health forced him to retire, and his church was filled to the brim with folks wanting to honor him with plaques and gifts."

"Well deserved, I'm sure," commented Gerald.

"Yes, he was loved by many. As I recollect, George earlier met the new preacher who'd take his place. The young fellow was nervous, even though he'd been praying and dreaming about pastoring a church all his life. Seems he'd received a few mean-spirited, unsigned letters from some folks warning he'd not be allowed to stay."

"Why in the world would anybody do such a thing?" Gerald asked.

"Well, sometimes change can bring out the worst in people. George wasn't having it and scrapped the message he'd prepared. Instead, he preached from his heart, which was what he was best known for, anyway. George's last sermon, spoken with an energy I hadn't heard in years, instructed the church on how to receive and encourage the new preacher. Most in the congregation were farmers, so he used an example they understood."

"I'm all ears," Gerald said with a smile.

"It went something like this." Jerry's pale blue eyes looked upwards with lips pursed slightly as he recalled and quoted George's words. "Folks, y'all know how to raise chickens, I'm sure. But do you know how to keep a rooster from crowing? You just put that strutting bird in a pen with a low top, so's he can't raise his head. He'll pull in great chestfuls of air to let out a heralding crow to do his job, announcing to the whole world God's dawn of another wonderful day. But he can't deliver with his head forced down. He'll keep trying to raise his beak skyward, again and again, until his crown is scratched and bleeding on that low ceiling, and he tuckers out."

Gerald chuckled at the story. "That's one way to sleep past five in the morning," he said, "but what does it have to do with welcoming a new preacher?"

"Well, the rooster can't crow. According to George, he looks forlornly at the new dawn, wondering how on earth the sun can rise and light up this beautiful world without his crowing to help it. It's a pitiful sight to behold, and preachers are much the same."

"How's that?" Gerald asked.

"God puts a word in preachers to share with others, and it's a powerful force in their nature to speak it out. It's their job, ordained by God Almighty. So, George said, 'Folks, you raise up the head of this young feller when he comes in here tonight! Don't put a low ceiling of glum faces or critical spirits over him, like the devil wants to do. You welcome him with open hearts and big smiles, him and his family. Listen with both ears and a whole heart to encourage him.

Then invite him to supper. If you really want to honor God, love on this young preacher.'"

"Just as a rooster's got to crow, a preacher's got to preach," Gerald said.

"Yes! So lift his head up! That's what Preacher George said."

Driving home, Johnny and Gerald both quietly reflected on Uncle Jerry's visit. "You know something, Johnny?" Gerald said in slowly measured tones, "Uncle Jerry and his brothers were the kind of men you and I should be like. He fought through World War I, came home to a pandemic, and saw his preacher brothers suffer all kinds of persecution back in the day, but none of them turned to booze or let life's troubles defeat them."

Johnny's eyes focused on his big brother.

"But me and you never had to go to war," Gerald continued. "We grew up in a stable society with all the comforts one could wish for. Shoot, our daddy even owned an ice cream store!" Gerald shot a wry smile at Johnny, who flashed back a toothy grin.

"And yet, little brother, we've been the ones to get divorced while chasing an unhealthy lifestyle, and missed out on raising our kids, even though Jeff lived with you awhile and my boys with me a few years. It looks like we gave up on striving to fulfill our destiny...whatever that may be. I believe it's high time you and me got on the ball. We've got big shoes to fill."

Johnny nodded in agreement, for those were his exact thoughts. He needed a change.

He'd been having unexplained periods of unrest and a chronic apathy towards usual fun activities. An uncharacteristic fog of disinterest stopped him in his tracks when planning events such as Saturday night billiards with old buddies. He'd get all foo-foo'd up to join Weldon at

Humphrey's Club for a night of pool, some light drinks, and socializing with pretty ladies who proudly sported plunging necklines and too much make-up. Then he'd sit in the parking lot staring blankly at the club like it was a mirage before driving home to call Weldon and lie about why he wouldn't show up.

Somewhere along life's roadway, the James Bond-ish fun, noisy excitement, and eye candy lost their allure. The initial thoughts or invitation to a night out perked him up, but the malaise of indifference crept in within the hour. This condition brought to mind a brightly painted storefront with dancing neon lights he'd visited as a boy, but once inside, he'd discovered an atmosphere of bland dullness and worn-out furnishings.

Partying lost its siren song, becoming unworthy of Johnny's time and the extra splashes of cologne.

Ditto for his favorite sports. His hunting craze, sparked during boyhood, became only an excuse to go to the woods for a walk. Many times his rifle remained uncased. Watching college football dwindled to monotony by halftime. Even some extra-curricular pursuits, common to avowed bachelors such as himself, left an unreasonable hollowness after the conquest. Shame grew as self-respect dwindled.

Were he a member of the James Bond 007 club, the membership would be abruptly revoked.

Troubled and perplexed at these mysterious changes which robbed him of sleep, Johnny sought a diversionary project to occupy his time and mind. He decided to install a Mercury-vapor light over Mother's greenhouse. She loved looking at the variety of flowers enclosed therein, but her meager porch light wasn't positioned to illuminate the colorful blooms after sunset.

Mother was excited to spend time with her son, describing newly-potted flowers while handing tools at his request during the install. Taking a break from the heat, Johnny joined her for a cup of coffee as Sister arrived to bring completed tax statements for Zestos. As the others chatted happily about church and family, he quietly sipped his caffeine. Mother still made Ted's preferred strong Cajun-style chicory coffee. She noticed his despondent mood.

"What's wrong, Johnny?" she asked after a spell. "You aren't acting like yourself today." She persisted even after several denials from her son, for a mother's instinct knows when a child, young or old, is troubled. Sister looked at him with a sweet but concerned expression.

"Please," Johnny sighed, staring at a wall clock with a wooden-paddled rustic mill scene set by a lazy streamside and wishing he was there. "Don't y'all worry about me. Yes, things are not going so well at the moment, and I'm not sure why. I know that life has hills and valleys. Right now, I'm in a low valley, but I'm sure it won't last. In no time, I'll be back on the hilltop again." Johnny tried a lopsided grin of assurance, but he sensed it wasn't convincing.

"Son, you need Jesus. Why don't you give the Lord a chance in your life?" Vida Mae pleaded in a gentle tone with a mother's love reflecting from her blue eyes.

"I truly don't know why, Mother. I pray to the Lord and believe in him. But something I can't explain holds me back from a full commitment. Maybe I feel I don't have what it takes to live the Christian life," Johnny admitted. "I really don't know," he concluded lamely, as one conceding defeat.

"We'll be saying extra prayers for you, Johnny, and the Good Lord will lift you out of this valley." Sister asserted, then brightened as she remembered something.

"Speaking of prayer, did Mother tell you what happened at church on Sunday?"

Johnny peered at Vida Mae with a puzzled expression.

"I was praying about Ted," Mother began after a slight

pause. "There remained in me some doubt as to his being in Heaven. Though he's been gone 16 years, I still love your daddy so much! The possibility of his missing out on eternal life burdened my soul. It all came spilling out while kneeling at my pew. I couldn't help myself, and prayers came rushing out of me like my heart grew its own voice." Mother's eyes blinked and peered slightly upward, as if reliving the intensity of that prayer.

"Though closed eyes, I detected a bright light coming from the church's arched window beside me. When I opened my eyes to see what was happening, it was as if the window opened up onto a scene of astonishing beauty, like a golden curtain drawing to begin a play. There stood a crowd of people mingling together in the most lovely scenery you can imagine, with folks smiling and rejoicing, singing a song I'd never heard. The music sounded sweet beyond words. Two of the people turned toward me, and I recognized Momma and Papa!"

Her children listened with rapt attention. "Tell him what happened then!" Sister said impatiently.

"Momma said, 'Hello, daughter!' and she looked young and healthy. All I could think to say was, 'Is Ted there?' to which Papa said, 'Yes, he's here.' Papa turned to look back like Ted was behind him when the scene started fading. I tried to ask if Gerald and Johnny were coming home, but by the time I got the words out, it was all gone as quickly as it had formed. There was only the usual church window in its place."

Tears glistened as she looked first at Sister, then to Johnny. "It was a most revealing vision, and the words sounded exactly like Momma and Papa's voices. The Lord's shown me wonderful and merciful things in my lifetime, but never a vision until now. I'm no longer worried about Ted. I've been given complete peace."

Driving home with Mother's stunning vision on his mind, Johnny wondered why God never responded to him in such a supernatural way. *Probably because I'm not living in obedience to God's word,* he reasoned. He'd enjoyed Mother and Sister's company, but the annoying feeling of unrest, like something important was missing, returned to vex his spirit by the time he arrived home.

Johnny imagined a beady-eyed buzzard circling over his head, awaiting the final throes of happiness and hope before scavenging what should've been a promising future.

Arriving home, he turned on the TV, hoping to view something that would divert his troubling thoughts. "The Searchers" starring John Wayne was playing. The theme song lyrics seemed written for him: "A man was made to wander, searching way out there. Peace of mind he knows he'll find, but where, Oh Lord, Lord where?"

Changing channels, a documentary dealing with air combat during World War II, caught his attention. The focus was an eyewitness account of an American bomber pilot stationed in England with the U.S. 8th Air Force. The silver-haired ex-pilot, Carl, sat on a stool under studio lights wearing his war-era uniform, recalling the crews' extreme dangers while making daily bombing runs over Nazi Germany.

Carl's honest features and clear-eyed, articulate expressions captivated Johnny's attention. Like all baby boomer men, war stories fascinated him. Many of his favorite coaches, relatives, and close neighbors were WWII vets. He greatly respected and admired them.

"We'd have a quick pre-dawn flight meeting before boarding our planes, and the jitters would start," Carl recalled. "At that time, our fighter-plane escorts didn't have the fuel capacity for a round trip from England to Germany, so they turned back over France. We hoped the rising sun behind us would blind enemy ground gunners, but still, their fighter planes rose to meet us, and our casualties were high."

Old film footage appeared on the screen, showing formations of American bombers, with one engulfed in flames, spiraling slowly downward from a smoky sky. Johnny was mesmerized, watching little flaming objects emerge from the fuselage of the falling plane, and he realized with a start they were burning airmen bailing out of the hellish interior of the doomed aircraft. He felt himself transported in time and experienced a painful revulsion as his heart commiserated with those poor flame-engulfed airmen whose screams of agony went unheard as they tumbled thousands of feet to the yearned-for release of death. He imagined the fear of surviving crews watching this.

As if reading his mind, Carl said, "This carnage went on with every mission flown, and I'd wake up nights with chills, looking around at empty bunks in our Quonset hut of friends who'd never fly again, never laugh again. The fears mounted day by day until I literally froze in place while walking to a pre-flight meeting one morning. I couldn't take another step; couldn't hardly even breathe."

Johnny jolted upright from a reclining position on his couch at those words, for a small voice in his head clearly said, *Fear is also your problem, but you can't see it.*

Angered at this insult, Johnny's macho was about to speak out that at six foot three inches and 240 pounds, he was NOT scared when the voice interrupted. *Carl was afraid of dying, but you're afraid of living. It's the same fear. You're afraid tomorrow will be as empty as today, and you'll grow old without any meaning to life — which is a form of death.*

Shocked and stunned at this idea, Johnny swung his legs off the couch, glaring wide-eyed at the TV. He wanted to throw a brick through it. The anger subsided as he reluctantly came to grips with the growing awareness of this unkind truth. "Yes," he admitted softly, "that's it. That's what's been bugging me. Things in life don't matter. They're hollow. Empty. Tomorrow is hopelessly patterned to be the same, and I am running away from it."

When lost in the woods and afraid as a boy, he wanted to be found. Now, as an adult, he was subconsciously looking to get lost from life. He wished he could run through those beautiful woods again and never stop. Fear, though more subtle than before, was again playing him.

"Nothing with meaning is something to fear. No matter how big you are," he whispered with a sense of awe, like someone uncovering an ugly object of surprising value.

Johnny glanced at the TV, and at that moment, Carl said something that changed Johnny's life.

"Being paralyzed with fear, I didn't know what to do with myself," Carl said as the camera focused on his face. "So, I said, 'Oh Lord, help me!' and out of the darkness, a voice, an audible voice just like I'm speaking now, answered me."

Johnny leaned forward in anticipation.

"The voice said, 'Carl, be not afraid. For I am with you

always, even unto the end of time.'"

Resounding throughout Johnny's soul, those words emitted not just from the television speaker but swirled from every direction round-about, tumbling from walls, floor, and ceiling. The source wasn't electronic or the effect one-dimensional, which was usually received through auditory perception and cerebral analysis. The message soaked in through every pore of his skin and coursed like an electrical current into Johnny's inner being, looking for a place to be grounded.

A non-biological sense within Johnny perceived a very special power involved. The message carried forth incredible beauty and brilliance of a life-altering promise anchored in love, spanning not only the 46 years of utterance during the war to Carl, but from the beginning of creation to beyond eternity.

There was an extravagantly powerful presence in the room. Johnny's whole being felt electrified and transformed, no longer shadowed by the vulture of emptiness.

Peace and wonder filled his heart and soul.

From the TV, Carl's voice declared, "All the fear drained out of me when I heard that, like water poured from a barrel. I walked to the pre-flight meeting and calmly flew my mission. Our plane was shot up several times, but I flew many more missions, completing the rest of the war without sustaining a scratch. "

Awed in his spirit, Johnny knew what he must do. He rolled off the couch, and his knees hit the floor. An unbidden resistance flared in his mind at the change taking place. The old persuasion that ruled him for years reminded Johnny what he'd have to give up was unrealistic for a guy like him. A guy whose habitual lifestyle included intimacy with women, telling dirty jokes with cuss words that sounded manly...and friends who relished the same. Pride would be most difficult to give up. "False pride," as Daddy used to caution him about, Johnny recalled. A man full of false pride resents any inference of fear. He can't deal with it. Nor does such a man embrace the humility required to surrender completely to God, wherein he may then be enabled to overcome fear.

Rebuking this old persuasion with heavy irony, Johnny sharply retorted, "Oh yeah! I sure would miss all these old, wonderful ways that so enrich a man, wouldn't I? Ha! I don't care what I have to give up! I do not belong to this culture anymore or to me anymore. I am now the Lord's —even unto the end of time."

Head bowed, Johnny confessed and repented of all he could remember of his disobedience to God. It was a long list. In the end, he asked for and was faithfully assured he received forgiveness by the resurrecting blood of Jesus Christ and was confident God would direct his life.

Johnny then recalled a quote from Thoreau that had haunted him for the last 20 years:

> *Most men live lives of quiet desperation, and go to the grave with their song still in them.*

Smiling broadly, he now envisioned those dead-end words bound at the foot of the cross, as a great composer wrote a new and joyous melody in his soul. A melody of life his heart would belt out in the days to come with more gusto than the Mormon Tabernacle Choir singing the Hallelujah Chorus.

He felt like a long-distance runner who'd trailed the pack for miles but received his "second wind" and now surged across the finish line. The First Place trophy was being placed in his raised hands while a heavenly host cheered wildly. Surely Momma and Papa were among them, along with Gerald. Perhaps Daddy's booming voice was echoing across heavenly counties, cheering on his son as in days past. He breathed in the fresh air of victory, and Johnny's heart filled with the assurance he'd find and fulfill God's purposes in the days ahead, contributing to and prospering within an inheritance incorruptible.

Peace was now written over the door to the future.

***

Several years of sobriety worked positive changes in Gerald's lifestyle. After working with Nancy in west Houston for two years and after a year of courtship, he remarried. She exhibited a quick sense of humor and, like Gerald, had two children from a previous marriage. Both waited until they were sure of the relationship before tying the knot. Gerald held nothing back about his past. She found his multi-faceted, brilliant intellect fascinating and was charmed by his modest and respectful attitude. Gerald proved the chivalrous gentleman she'd imagined as a girl becoming a mate someday. She did, however, put her foot down on one subject.

"One thing I must tell you, Gerald," Nancy informed him after dinner the night she accepted his proposal. "I can't contemplate living this stage of life with an alcoholic. Any support I can give you to remain sober, I will. You can count on that. I'd never leave you, but it would be a terrible hurt should I ever witness your return to the bottle. Please remember that."

"I understand perfectly," Gerald assured her. "You know by now I am a man of strong will, and my will is to live out life in absolute sobriety."

Church attendance became a routine, and Gerald did return to his roots, believing (with some uncertainty and limited commitment) in God again. Yet, he felt he had not accomplished the leap of faith necessary to be convinced God works supernaturally in the lives of His children. To his engineering mind, scientific laws held sway, and God worked only through this structure. As a result, Gerald depended upon his own will and knowledge to stay the "Master of his ship, and the Captain of his soul." Gerald had been too long trained in his vocation to not take the bit in his own mouth and determine the outcomes for desired success.

He was still the boss. His own mind defined success.

After several years working as a computer hardware and software analyst, he was given an emergency, top-priority directive from Stewart & Stevenson. A firm in the Netherlands had purchased several massive power-generating turbines, but they failed after installation and a short run time.

Panic-stricken communications rushed across the Atlantic when the European specialists couldn't diagnose or troubleshoot the problem. Their experts were stumped, unable to determine if the glitch was related to hardware or software. They needed help, and they needed it badly.

Hastily packed and given carte blanche by his company, Gerald boarded a jet armed with full discretionary power and unlimited financial resources to get the folks in Den Haag back on the grid. The acronym ASAP was voiced a dozen times in the company's brief to Gerald.

Upon arrival, Gerald was rushed to the turbines, and a plethora of white-frocked, bespectacled technicians and computer specialists hovered closely around him. Gerald had an amusing impression of noisy seagulls fluttering around a shrimp boat in Galveston Bay.

Within three hours, Gerald located the problematic software source and corrected the issue. A collective sigh of regeneration was shared on both sides of the ocean, and both Gerald and Stewart & Stevenson were lauded copiously by the Danes. Gerald was chauffeured back to his five-star hotel, where he donned evening wear for preparations to dine in the most exclusive restaurant in Denmark.

Halfway through the evening, a bottle of vintage champagne was uncorked to toast the wondrous success of their visiting American ex-NASA genius. Gerald didn't want to chance insulting custom by refusing to partake, so he agreed to just one sparkling goblet.

He awoke the next morning with a hotel valet shaking him vigorously and in broken English, telling him his flight home would board in 90 minutes.

Looking through bloodshot eyes at his rumpled, food-stained suit, Gerald wondered what he'd done and said the night before. There was no memory available after 10 p.m. With the jabbering valet helping him undress, Gerald noticed glitter under his own fingernails and tried not to imagine the source of that. An erotic tattoo parlor business card fell from a pocket. He experienced a dread that matched the intensity of his torturous headache as to what work of art may be revealed upon undressing. An undefined substance with a vile odor crusted his shoes.

The jet banked west as Gerald tried to keep his churning stomach from convulsing. He paid no heed to the first-class seating arrangements, for his state was one of wretched misery. No physical luxury could alleviate it. The cuff on his sweater looked odd before he realized the sweater was inside-out.

"Is the bathroom occupied? "Gerald croaked hoarsely to a stewardess, as he doubted his shaking legs could make two trips there.

"I shall see, sir, "she replied, recoiling from his caustic breath and spider-veined eyes.

After losing his dinner from the night before, Gerald sat

upon the toilet in complete despair. Recounting his experience to Johnny weeks later, he declared, "That's the sickest I've ever been. I'd of had to get better to die." Yet the worst torment was from not knowing what he'd done or said while drunk and to what extent would be the consequences. For all he knew, he may have terribly embarrassed or insulted his hosts. If so, his employer would hear of it and probably lose millions of dollars worth of business.

Termination would include a black-balling of Gerald, ruining his name and reputation throughout the industry. Nancy would find out along with his sons, Steve and David...and everybody else. Nancy would be devastated, and the church would invite him to leave the congregation.

For the first time in his life, Gerald admitted to himself he could not act responsibly by the power of his own will alone. He'd sworn never to drink again, but the euphoria of success along with the admiration of his Danish peers lured him into assuming he could stop with one drink. No matter that he'd been years sober, resisting numerous urges by strength of will, just as he'd quit tobacco, which doctors claimed was a tougher addiction. But now he needed help. And just like the Danes earlier, he needed it ASAP. His hurting heart told him there was only one source for it.

An incidental memory then came to mind while he sat in the jet's bathroom. He could almost hear, once again, his mother's voice from 30 years ago blending with Momma and Papa's as they sweetly sang, "I have decided to follow Jesus, no turning back, no turning back." Gerald realized he had turned back in life, away from Jesus, mistakenly seeking another way.

Despairing of losing all he held dear due to a deceptively weak human will, Gerald returned to Jesus Christ in the bathroom of a jet flying at high altitude over the Atlantic. A man who'd craved the freedom of high-flying all his life was about to experience it on the ultimate level.

He prayed with an impoverished heart, a nauseous body, and a humbled spirit. While praying, Gerald felt the hand of salvation work in his soul, and he knew with certainty of three things upon saying, "Amen."

One, Gerald was not in the least bit sick in either his stomach, head, or body. He was made instantly well. Two, he'd felt the spirit of God assure him all would be okay back home. His family would not turn their backs on him. Three, He was absolutely certain the burden of alcoholism was forever lifted.

No turning back, no turning back.

Changing his sweater around, he felt like more than a garment was no longer inside-out. Something else had been made right, and the fit was perfect, tailor-made by Gerald's Creator. He recalled at that moment the story in Luke of a son who'd strayed from home. And just as the father welcomed home the prodigal son, Gerald felt welcomed home in the same manner. Welcomed back in the spirit of love, of mercy, and of amazing grace.

Little did he know that when his hosts brought him unconscious back to the hotel, Vida Mae was at church praying with their lady's group in a time zone seven hours behind The Netherlands. A visiting speaker named Sister Rose was known for having the gift of prophecy.

Concluding the meeting, she prayed with every lady individually. Upon grasping Vida Mae's hand, Sister Rose opened her eyes wide, exclaiming, "You are one of God's great intercessors and have been since childhood, so be encouraged. Let's pray together now for that which is heavy upon your heart, and God will surely hear us. "

Vida Mae simply said, "Yes, pray with me over my son, Gerald. He is a long way from home and, though he attends church, is too long away from the Lord. "

Nancy noticed a difference in Gerald when he arrived home. His smile sparkled more than usual, and his carriage appeared to have extra bounce walking through airport security. Before telling her about his experiences overseas, Gerald checked in with his employer. By all reports, their customer was very satisfied with his expertise and performance. He'd be welcomed back anytime. Gerald relayed this to Nancy, and on a whim, gave her a full report of everything. Everything.

Both were at peace by the end of the conversation. It became apparent as they talked that what seemed initially to be a disastrous event, God turned for a good purpose.

Vida Mae was overjoyed. Both sons were no longer estranged from her Lord. She wished Ted had lived to see this; then realized that in due time he would, for all will rejoin in Heaven.

That day came sooner than expected for one in the family.

During Thanksgiving dinner, Johnny noticed Gerald rubbing a bump on his collarbone. When asked about it, Gerald said the small knot came up the previous week and was tender to the touch. He made a doctor's appointment for next week.

On the 16th anniversary of his daddy's funeral, Gerald's family received the alarming news he had an invasive, advanced tumor in the right lung. Johnny remembered Daddy's prophetic words, repeated often while glaring at the smoking cigarette between his calloused fingers: "These dang things will kill me someday."

With a chilling premonition, Johnny envisioned another tearful cemetery gathering of broken hearts. A flash of anger at the tobacco industry darkened his features while a sense of injustice brewed in his conscious. Daddy was given 62 years of life. Gerald was only 52. He was too young to go.

Daddy at least knew his grandchildren well, except for only three years with Jeffrey. David's little girl, Amanda, who was yet but five, was the only grandchild Gerald would know.

They deserved more time together. They all deserved better. Death is the vilest of all thieves, he decided. Johnny's hands balled into fists.

Seeing his brother's angst, Gerald calmly informed everyone of an experimental treatment available for his particular cancer that showed promise. A referral set up a consultation, and Gerald was scheduled to begin applications of concentrated heatwaves electronically produced to target tissue constituting his tumor. Everyone perked up at this news, and hope stirred the glum atmosphere like a fresh wind from the piney woods.

For the next two months, Johnny drove Gerald to downtown Houston's Medical Center for hour-long treatments. The device used resembled ping pong paddles, placed behind and in front of his upper chest. The heat generated scalded Gerald's skin, but he withstood it heroically, allowing not even a slight grimace. The technician administering treatment commented to Johnny one day, "Your brother is quite a man!"

"Of course he is. He's an Anderson," Johnny replied casually but with a flush of pride.

The brothers shared a lot of each other's hearts during these trips. Gerald was somewhat weakened, for he'd undergone chemotherapy along with the other treatments, but his mind was clear and his love for "Little Big Brother," as he called Johnny, sprouted like new spring grass.

"Johnny," he said thoughtfully one morning, "you need to go back to college."

"Gerald, I'm 40 years old. I'd look silly sitting in class with a bunch of teeny-boppers!"

"So?" Gerald countered quickly.

"I work full time. And I help Mother sometimes at Zestos. And I have a house with a yard to take care of. Plus, my dog, Beau, has to be fed and watered," Johnny spouted hastily.

"So?" Gerald repeated with a laconic sideways glance, indicating he saw through the lame excuses.

"I don't know, Gerald. Not sure I could cut it. Been out of school 20 years. However, maybe some maturity has finally taken root. Could be time to give it a try. Remember what Daddy used to say about me? "Johnny's a late bloomer. He'll be 30 years old before he has a lick of sense!" Johnny laughed.

"Sure, I remember him saying that," Gerald said with a smile. Then he turned and, with a mock-serious expression, stated, "But Daddy was wrong about that." When Johnny glanced his way, expecting something complimentary to clarify this, Gerald said, "He was off by ten years. You were 40 before you had a lick of sense! That's this year, so use your late-blooming sense and go back to school!"

The brothers giggled like kids all the way home at this exchange.

Good health was returning to Gerald over the next few months as his lung tumor shrunk. Doctors gave him a positive prognosis, predicting the cancer would be overcome entirely and he'd live many more years.

They were wrong.

Gerald became violently sick one day at home and was rushed to his doctor. Tests revealed he had a large tumor in the liver. Two weeks later, the family was advised to "make arrangements."

Becoming weaker, Gerald confided in Johnny that the days were getting shorter and made a request. "Take care of Mother and Sister for me. You'll have to be strong for them when this comes to an end."

"I will, Gerald. Just like you would if this was reversed,"

Johnny replied, noticing with wonder how Gerald's blue eyes appeared more striking than ever. His spirit couldn't be suppressed by encroaching death.

There was no evidence whatsoever of fear. Only peace received from grace.

Johnny drove to the hospital after work on April 18, 1991, knowing he'd see his brother for the last time in this world. Though his big brother was in a coma during the visit, he took Gerald by the hand and told him many things. For the first time ever, Johnny told Gerald how much he loved him. While saying goodbye, he finished with, "Gerald, all my life, you've bragged on your " little big brother" because I grew taller and bigger than you. But I always looked up to you. Always busted the buttons off my shirt with pride in you. Still do. In my eyes, you are a giant."

Very softly, with hardly any pressure felt, Gerald squeezed Johnny's hand. Little big brother recalled hearing stories that only Gerald's holding his hand would silence his cries when he was a baby. Johnny felt that effect again.

All that night, Johnny prayed for strength. When the early morning call came, he was prepared. Arriving at the hospital, he found Mother and Sister already comforted. The strength he'd prayed for and received was given to them as well. They hugged and supported Nancy.

At Gerald Cay Anderson's funeral, a well-dressed gentleman came to Vida Mae and, after expressing his condolences, said to her, "I used to work with Gerald. You'll never know how much good your son did at NASA. He was very involved with developing a solution to save the lives of those astronauts on Apollo 13." With that, he left without signing the guest register.

Johnny later tried to research the identity of this man and uncover details of which he'd spoken concerning Gerald's involvement in Apollo 13. Years later, Nancy ran across an ex-NASA employee, McQueen, who gave her more details. It seems that Gerald gathered together three of his best programmer-engineers, and the four of them designed and wrote emergency programs to analyze data being sent back to NASA from the stranded astronauts. These programs enabled a resolution to successfully return the spacecraft home, saving the lives of James Lovell, John Swiggert, and Fred Haise.

Vida Mae sold Zestos that December, after 42 years in business. Another era had passed.

***

San Jacinto College offered a good curriculum, so Johnny enrolled in evening classes the semester following Gerald's death. He endured the dreaded orientation with much trepidation, relaxing upon discovering other mature students in the group.

He prayed about Gerald's notion of resuming higher education during middle age and felt this was a good move. To his surprise, most courses were not very difficult as he had a good high school education from 23 years prior. Only Algebra proved a toughie, and he took pre-algebra several times before a light came on. Johnny graduated with an associate's degree.

Before his last semester, Johnny felt a change in his perspective on marriage. More and more, he noticed married couples enjoying their children at shopping malls, restaurants, and local parks as he jogged by. It looked like a good life, no longer something to avoid. The Lord was working in his heart, creating the urge to share and give the specially-designed part of a man that makes a husband and father. Eyes once darkened by hurt and divorce were being healed, and he glimpsed the notion of a union in a better light. His 20-year vow to never marry again began to dim.

Vida Mae called to tell him she and other ladies from church were loading up to leave for a women's retreat in Kerrville. She casually mentioned they prayed for one another during the six-hour drive, and she would ask prayers for him to find a Christian wife. Expecting Johnny's usual fast denial about matrimony, Vida Mae was shocked at his reply.

"I would appreciate that very much, Mother," he said easily.

"What!?" Vida Mae exclaimed. "Do you mean that?"

"Yes, ma'am."

"Well then! You can be sure we will. Oh, you make me so happy, son! This is the best news I've heard all week. I'll call you when we get back Sunday night."

When Johnny checked his mail the next afternoon, he noticed a letter from his insurance company regarding the roof on his house. It implied he'd need a new roof within three months, or they'd discontinue coverage. Johnny was irate, for his roof was fine, and he immediately drove to the local agent to discuss this. Once there, he was referred to a specialist, Miss Susie Marler.

Upon entering her office, Johnny noticed a very businesslike, lovely blond. She invited him to sit down while she read the letter with a kind smile showing dimpled cheeks. He saw a portrait of three good-looking kids on her desk and no wedding ring on her left hand. Johnny was no longer irate. By the end of their conversation, he was trying to hide his enchantment.

Several months later, he took Susie and the kids, Amanda, Patrick, and Steffie, to the Anderson camp near Woodville. After sundown, Johnny and Susie left the kids eating supper around the campfire for a short drive outside the gate where the neighboring 1000 acres had been clear-cut of all timber.

Shady Grove Church was located a half-mile east as they parked well outside of Johnny's treelined property. The sky view was expansive there, spectacularly starred in the pristine country air.

Susie Sumpter Marler, Johnny's future soul mate.

Putting his arm around Susie, Johnny set up his proposal by saying, "Did I ever tell you my mother prayed for me a wife just before I received that insurance letter, and we met?"

With a flash in her eyes, Susie exclaimed, "What a coincidence! My ex-mother-in-law was praying for a husband for me that week!"

"Guess this relationship was okay'd by the Good Lord,

huh?" Johnny said softly. "You reminded me of someone when we first met. Now I know who it is. My second wife."

I thought you were only married once," Susie stated.

"That's right."

"Is that a proposal, Johnny Anderson?" the dimples inquired.

"I've been proposing in my heart to you for months. This is just the first time using words."

Her warm kiss said "Yes" better than words, and the stars sparkled all the brighter.

As they settled back to stand arm in arm, gazing at the millions of brilliant stars, a streak of light like a brightly burning arrow burst forth from their left, emerging out of the dark treelined western horizon. The shooting star traversed the entire sky from west to east as if shot from some giant celestial archer, blazing a fiery trail with purplish highlights directly towards the heavens above Shady Grove Church. Johnny and Susie stood entranced for several silent moments, awed by the magnificent display.

"Beautiful!" Susie whispered reverently, still looking upward.

"Yes, Beautiful indeed," breathed Johnny, taking into his heart and soul the absolute magic of God's stunning display of heavenly splendor and of the human heart's music accompanying the entire scene, composing a love song joining man and woman.

"I take this as a sign that God approves," Johnny uttered before kissing his fiancée again.

On March 31, 1995, Johnny and Susie wed. All three kids, Amanda, Patrick and Steffanie, partook in their vows.

Patrick, Amanda & Steffanie join in with the marriage of their mom to Johnny.

After a year, Johnny and Susie agreed they wanted more children. Although Johnny was a bit long in the tooth, Susie was 13 years younger and still of child-bearing age. Johnny remembered his grandfather Anderson had been 58 years old when Ted, his youngest of 16 kids, was born. Johnny wanted a second chance to do things right and raise a child from a baby to adulthood — something he had not done with Jeff.

Their first pregnancy ended tragically in miscarriage. Susie's doctor ran medical tests afterward, but no conclusive reason was found for the baby not making it to full term.

Her doctor decided it was 'just one of those things' and mentioned waiting a while to recover, then trying again.

Everything went smoothly during the first four months of their second pregnancy, and the couple felt assured they'd have a healthy child. Then Susie started spotting one Saturday evening, and they drove to a hospital in Baytown. Later that night, they lost their second baby. Both were heartbroken.

"Your wife is recovering well, but we suggest she remain here overnight. You can check her out of the hospital around 9:00 a.m. if no complications arise," Susie's doctor advised. Johnny agreed and left after Susie went into a troubled sleep.

Walking to the parking lot, Johnny suffered a stabbing pang of guilt. It was an old adversary stirred up again from the little life just lost. He remembered some dark events of his bachelor years during his 20s. He'd been a party to two abortions. Those performing the abortions referred to the tiny life as "tissue", making the whole awful procedure sound normal. Reading the Bible years later, Johnny's heart broke while realizing that God gives life, tenderly and lovingly forming babies in their mother's womb. Pregnancy was not simply the result of man and woman getting together, with a living human being's existence starting only outside the birth canal. It is a life formed by intent and for the purposes of God Almighty from the first fusing of cells. The horrific truth about abortion is that it is murder.

The burden of guilt was more than he could stand.

"Oh God, oh merciful God, please forgive me!" Johnny's prayer exploded within the cab of his truck. He seized the steering wheel in an iron grip and shook it so hard the entire extended-cab truck rocked side to side. A nurse walking casually by looked askance in Johnny's direction and abruptly quickened her pace. "I'm so sorry. Please forgive me and don't visit my guilt upon Susie. If this is because I've helped kill two children, please let this be the end of retribution! "

After sitting there a while, Johnny made a covenant with God, unable to bear the thought of him and Susie not having children.

"Lord, if You can see your way to give us a child, here's what I promise to do. I will be a godly dad to that child. I'm not sure exactly what all that means, but I am sure of a few things. If You give us a child, I will raise that child in your way and will take that child to church. Daddy always wanted me to go to church, but for some reason, he didn't go. When our child turns around in church to look, he or she will see Dad there."

Johnny clenched his hands as he prayed.

"If you'll give us a child, that child will never see dad drink one drop of liquor. I know drunkenness won't condemn someone to Hell. But some people are prone to alcoholism. I will not be an example of drinking booze in front of our children and chance influencing them to a life of addiction. As of this instant, I will never touch another drop. That's a promise."

In his fervor, he wiped at the sting of hot tears that threatened to spill from his closed eyes.

"If you'll give us a child, that child will never see me strike Susie, no matter what. Nor will that child ever hear me call her a curse name. I will respect her and teach our child that same respect. And that's all I can think of, Lord. It's in your hands. These are my promises to you. I've read in the Bible that Mother gave me, your mercies last forever. So, I place Susie and myself, and our future child, and those two little children who never had a chance at life here but who are with You now, upon your mercy. In Christ's name, I pray. Amen."

Johnny wiped the tears off his truck's steering wheel and

drove slowly home, catching every traffic light green.

Susie's doctor again found no cause for the miscarriage, and they were led to a doctor across town at the Women's Hospital of Houston. That doctor ran some tests that turned up negative before Susie mentioned an unusual condition she'd read about. He agreed to test for lowered levels of progesterone. After months of tests and administered medicine, Dr. Irwin gave Susie the green light. The whole family prayed diligently for a healthy, full-term pregnancy.

She became pregnant a third time. On August 4, 1998, one week after Johnny's 48th birthday and one week before Norma Jean's 61st birthday, Travis Anderson was born with his dad watching in the delivery room. Johnny was allowed to carry his son downstairs to be weighed and measured. His joy was unmatched by any other new dad in the hospital, and prayers of thanksgiving rose continually from his lips.

Susie became pregnant again within the year, even though the couple wasn't trying yet for another baby. They were ecstatic at the news. Two months after finding out they were expecting a girl, Susie awoke with a start and shook Johnny awake. Both were talking earlier about a girl's name but had not made a decision. "I know what to name our baby, now. We'll name her Faith, "she said with finality.

"How did you come up with that name?" Johnny asked, rubbing his eyes.

"I just had a dream that God told me to name her Faith."

"Who told you? Did you say God?" Johnny queried, now fully awake.

"Yes, and it's the most vivid dream I've ever had. I'm sure it was God."

Johnny never heard Susie say God told her anything (and he never heard her say that again), so he didn't dismiss it as a fluke. "Okay. We'll name her Faith. Now let's get some rest."

On March 31, 2000, Johnny and Susie's fifth wedding anniversary, Faith Anderson was born, beautiful and healthy, sporting dimples like her mom. Johnny felt overwhelmed with gratitude. He'd asked God's mercy for a child. But God, in his marvelous grace, gave them two children. This left a lasting impression. Although he didn't know God's will as to having more children, he could count on God's wisdom, goodness, and mercy.

Discussing this with Mother, Johnny admitted he'd seriously thought about giving up hope of having children after the first miscarriage. The idea conflicted with his firm belief God had put them together in marriage. It was obviously God's will. And because of this, he'd assumed it was also God's will that they completed the union with children to increase the family.

Children of promise, Travis and Faith complete the family."

"Did I ever tell you about the time I almost quit and sold the store?" Mother asked.

"I don't think so," Johnny replied.

"You remember how God answered my prayer about Zestos when Ted passed away, and God revealed his will that I was to stay open and not quit."

Johnny nodded.

"Well, a few years later, I had a series of equipment breakdowns and employee problems. My time and thoughts were so fixated on the business that I completely forgot about an important church service and business meeting that night at Greens Bayou Assembly. I promised to give a ride to some friends, and by the time I remembered, there was little time to go home, change clothes, and get them before the meeting started."

"Oh no!" Johnny exclaimed, knowing how conscientious his mother was.

"Well, I was fit to be tied! I hated the idea that Zestos had become more important than honoring God and honoring my word. A man at church frequently offered to buy the store, so on the drive home, I cried out to God for forgiveness and told him that I was quitting and would sell that stupid store when the meeting adjourned."

"What happened then?" Johnny asked.

"The most amazing thing. A voice said, 'Don't quit.' It scared me out of my wits, I can tell you! I wheeled off the feeder road into Kmart's parking lot, stopped my car, and looked to see who was in the backseat. Nobody there. Then I knew who said this. I was so scared I could barely speak, but I did, managing to squeak out, "But Lord, it's taking too much from me. It's making me miss church!"

Johnny noticed the mix of frustration and awe in her voice.

"And that calming voice said, 'You are right where I want

you to be. You are doing good unto others. You are giving the world a smile.' Hearing the actual voice of God was such a humbling experience. I guess I never shared this because I figured folks would think I was crazy! But, Johnny, I'm telling you it happened just that way."

Johnny nodded, enthralled at her story and wondering if God would ever speak directly to him.

"It was then I realized the importance of persistence when one is dedicated to serving God. We can't always understand his will on every matter, but we must trust that he will move us when the time's right in his eyes. He will make that known. Until then, we're to bloom where we are planted. Even at a nerve-wracking business."

Johnny was captivated by Mother's testimony, and he recalled a statement made by Mother Teresa, the sainted lady of Calcutta who helped the poor street people get fed. She said, "A person with the Lord in their heart preaches without speaking."

Mother's genuine, loving smile cheered and encouraged untold numbers of customers through the decades and conveyed the goodness of God without words.

She represented him well.

Thinking of this later, Johnny considered returning to college for a bachelor's degree. Settling for an associate's degree seemed a bit like quitting. When Daddy and Mother worked hard at Zestos and came home nights exhausted, they'd talk about the sacrifice being for a good cause in that their kids could get a college education. Traditionally, this meant a four-year degree.

He and Susie owned an older home with ten acres of wooded land. The upkeep took a lot of work after their regular jobs. Susie agreed it would be good for him to return to school, but how could he manage the time to attend? After much prayer, Johnny heard about online courses becoming popular, and some degree plans could be pursued that way.

College student Travis with his niece, Skylar Brown.

After shopping around, Johnny decided on Corban College (which later became Corban University). They accepted all his previous credit hours from San Jacinto College. He and Susie bundled up little Travis and Faith and flew to Salem, Oregon, for Johnny to complete several days of orientation.

It took him three and a half years, but Johnny received confirmation he'd completed the degree plan for a Bachelor of Science. He couldn't wait to tell Mother the good news and intended to give the confirmation letter to her as a gift. Sister had a wonderful idea. She'd throw a birthday party for him at her house and invite Mother along with a dozen others in the family. Until then, they'd keep mum to Mother about his graduating.

Everybody enjoyed a great meal on the beautiful day Johnny turned 58. Mother was all smiles as he blew out one big candle on his cake. After stuffing their faces, it was time for unwrapping presents. Mother was asked to be last, and as she stepped forward to give her son the beautifully wrapped present, all eyes were focused their way, and the room became quiet.

"Before you give me that package, Mother, I have a present for you," Johnny said with slow deliberation and a steady gaze into her eyes.

"A present for me? But it's not my birthday!" She smiled in confusion.

"I know that, but it's a present that's been overdue for 30 years. It's a present that completes your and Daddy's dreams for your children. A dream you worked hard for, selling nickel ice cream cones every day and night while other couples went bowling or shopping or to the Friday night movies; and to Sunday church."

With that, he pulled a bag off the framed letter of notification certifying a BS degree, with the diploma due upon the end of semester graduation. "God has done it again, Mother. It's with great pride that I give this to you now and tell you that all three of your children are college graduates as of today. Some of us late bloomers take a little bit longer, I admit." He paused to allow the ripple of giggles to subside. "But we got it done. And I thank you from Sister and myself, and if I may, from Gerald too. I imagine him looking on from heaven with a big grin."

Vida Mae's smile could be seen for a country mile as she wiped away the copious tears and hugged her son for a long while. Johnny could feel the strong arms of Daddy blending with Mother's in that embrace. Dry eyes were a scarcity for the next few minutes.

Next to his returning to the Lord and the birth of his kids, it was one of the best days of Johnny's life.

Teenager Faith outshines the flowers.

***

Hearing the news of another major hurricane heading towards Texas, Johnny sharpened the blades on his chainsaw. There was a half-rotted tree behind their house he'd take down now, well ahead of the possible high winds. This was a lesson learned seven years ago in 2005, when Hurricane Rita blew into Texas as a category 3 storm. It was predicted to bypass them, so he didn't worry. Predictions changed, and Rita intensified, coming straight for the upper Texas Gulf Coast. Johnny decided they'd evacuate for their heavily treed property would look like a battlefield, and the risk for injury or death was too high to tolerate.

Faith was five, Travis seven, and Steffie 15. Three good reasons to put caution above the desire to stay home and protect from looters who exploited the mayhem of hurricanes. He was angry at himself for not removing a problem tree months before when his buddy, Carl Flowers, was there with his tractor. The big hackberry tree was 12 feet south of their home and had a distinct lean towards the house. To make matters worse, it had a case of heart-rot on the north trunk, increasing the odds for a direct hit on the house. Felling it with a chainsaw and no source of power to pull it east or west would most likely have disastrous results.

After packing Susie's Suburban and his truck, Johnny called the kids to gather around the hackberry tree. Prayer was the only solution now. The kids needed to learn early the value of committing life's issues to God. While Steffie helped Susie load family picture albums, Johnny had Travis and Faith place their hands alongside his on the rough bark of the threatening tree. Before closing his eyes, he took one last glance at the two little ones putting their trust in Dad and their little hands with his. Their faces looked as sweet as a spring sunrise over blue waters.

"Oh Lord, please hear our prayer for our home before this storm comes along. Susie and I prayed about moving here ten years ago, and you said yes. It's a good home. We've raised several children here and a few more to go. We gather together now and ask your mercy for protection over our lives and this home. Please, if you decide to bring this tree down, lay it either there (pointing east) or there (he pointed west) so it doesn't hit the house. But it's your land, and your house, and your tree. And Lord, we are your sons and daughters. We've agreed to put our trust in you, so please protect and bless all standing before you now. Enable us to live for you through all trials and seasons, in fair weather or foul. Get us to our destination and back home safely. Amen."

Susie holding Faith while walking in the country. This picture always reminded Johnny of the beauty of a mother's love!

Returning home a week later, they discovered various-sized limbs strewn everywhere on the ten acres and several trees broken, split, or uprooted. But not one big limb or tree was on the roof of their home or garage, or the water well.

Picking their way carefully through the debris, they spied the hackberry tree. It was broken off at ground level and had fallen east, the exact direction Johnny first pointed during their prayer.

This sweet memory of God's grace stirred Johnny to passionate prayers of thanksgiving. He reviewed the many blessings he'd received since returning to the Lord years earlier. Travis was now 15 and Faith 13, and both were healthy. As he gave thanks for his mother, he realized her 98th birthday was around the corner. With Daddy gone and Susie's dad also gone, he'd prayed for years that God would let Grandma Anderson have many days so Travis and Faith could know her well before she went home. God obviously had answered those prayers. He knew that Mother's last day could come at any time, and he wondered how to express a fitting tribute for such an amazing woman, who'd served an amazing God so faithfully for almost a century.

An idea came to him. He decided to begin composing what he'd say now and give it to her as a birthday present. She deserved to hear the high regard in which she was held now, not have them spoken when her ears were sealed in a casket. As he wrote, the words flowed out on their own.

Dear Mother,

As someone we knew and loved so well would say, if he were here, "Well, bust my britches! You've made it 98 years now!" Thinking of the wonderful legacy you and Daddy are leaving our family, I want to honor you on your birthday by reviewing the memories I cherish of us all, and the excellent outcomes of lives lived within the circle of loving prayers you've offered up so faithfully on our behalf. You made our home in Galena Park a happy place for a little boy. You used to sing, "It's time to get up, it's time to get up this morning!" so cheerfully each day that I woke up excited to be alive.

Everything seemed to make you laugh, our pets Pinky and Mickey Boy, Daddy's antics, and the way he joked with Sister and Gerald, and we laughed with you. I know now that God's spirit was the real substance of our laughter, for you honored Him then and now, and He blessed us.

Zestos prospered as well, and I grew with the business under your diligent eye and nurturing ways. As Pastor Granberry said, "They served love to an entire community at Zestos." You taught me to overcome shyness at Zestos' window and look customers in the eye, listen carefully to what they say, and be polite even when they're not. You taught me to care for people and to deal honestly with them. This godly teaching has served me well all my life.

I see now Zestos was a ministry, and the good done there for folks can't be measured in worldly terms. Daddy was the boss, but you were the foundation of Zestos. Thanks, Mother, for all that love, hard work, and reliability.

In my teen sports, you taught me that "A winner never quits and a quitter never wins." This was your life's motto. I attribute all of my advances in the sports arena to your encouragement. In short, you taught me to do my best, on the field and off.

We've had many good times in the country, at camp, and in the woods. Besides you and Sister, it's been a constant all through my life. You and Daddy taught me outdoor skills, but y'all also taught me to see the works of our Good Lord's hand in nature. In my adult years, during times I overly grieved about Daddy's death while making bad decisions, I could still see the reality of God while in our woods, for, "The invisible things of Him from the creation of the world are clearly seen." Thank you for teaching me to really see and love God's creation.

By the way, the little wild orchids you love so much still bloom in the bottomland. I smile every time I see them, and they'll remind me of you as long as I live.

So all three of your children completed college (1 a tad late), something you and Daddy always wanted and worked so hard toward. Something you never had the chance to do. I used to marvel at Sister's determination to excel in so many arenas simultaneously, climbing the academic ladder to a brilliant professional career while fulfilling her God-ordained purposes as a wife and mom. And investing time into the future of our youth and church. What magic motivated her?

And what got into Gerald that caused him to believe he could learn and do anything — be voted "Most Outstanding" at one of America's foremost universities, become an Olympic class diver, a musician, sail a boat, pilot a plane, and design a laser weapon defense system?

What made him think he could touch the moon?

After many years of observation, Mother, I'm convinced both were extraordinary because of your direct influence upon them, co-mingled with prayer, that let them, and me, always know you had absolute faith in your children. You had no doubts at all we could do anything we set our minds to do, and you conveyed this confidence vocally and spiritually every day.

You are the greatest motivator I've ever known, and if God hadn't already had the Apostle Paul write, "I can do all things through Christ who strengthens me," well, I'm sure He would've had you write it. Thank you, Mother, for believing in us.

Now in my 60s, I've been seeking God's face again for over two decades. Mother, I returned to Christ because of your and Sister's prayers and godly examples of faithful, obedient living. The Gospel had to be true, I realized, as I watched you live through both good times and the tragic losses of Daddy and Gerald, and still keep that beautiful smile shining God's love out to others. I wanted to have what you have inside. I wanted to give love out, not just take it in. My old way of thinking began to waver and dissolve when observing how much delight you took in family instead of things and by really listening to all your stories of our historical struggles as a unified family — and how God brought us through it all.

Following your example, I now have a close relationship with Jesus and a new resolve in life: to be a godly husband and dad, to live worthy of my Lord and my family, and for us to all be heaven bound. This resolve mirrors yours, as the scripture states, "Holding forth the word of life; that I may rejoice in the day of Christ, that I have not run in vain, neither labored in vain."

Mother, I'm very grateful to you for being all I've written here, and so much more, and please know I'll do my best to hand down to our kids the beautiful legacy that you and Daddy have left to me. You've truly not run in vain nor labored in vain, and the Lord is still using you and will do so, even when you're gone from here. That's what such a legacy does. He is blessing us through you, so enjoy this birthday, and know I love you dearly!

Your son,

Johnny

Four and one-half years later, Johnny drove to the hospice in Spring to visit Mother, who was now 102 years and five months of age. She'd been diagnosed with a spot in her lung that could be cancerous. The family decided not to have invasive surgery to get a sample, for she was now very frail. Her spirits were high, but the body was fading. Johnny knew the end was close.

When he entered her room, Sister and her daughter, Terri, were leaving. Mother's mouth was open, and the breathing ragged. He was taken aback at how much Mother appeared to have shrunken physically — an image made more noticeable by extra-puffy pillows.

As he sat to one side, watching the television at the foot of her bed, Johnny thought of all he'd like to tell her of his family. After 30 minutes of silence, he decided to talk as if she weren't comatose and could hear him. He began by telling her how pretty Faith was and that Travis seemed to be doing well his first year in college. Then he described Amanda's little baby, Skylar, and how the other three were growing so fast. He chattered away through the whole list of kids and grandkids and gave updates on baseball teams and funny happenings.

The ragged breathing stopped. Glancing to his left, Johnny was just in time to see Mother's eyes open. She raised her head off the pillow a few inches and turned her gaze to peer closely at her son sitting three feet away.

In her normal non-whispery voice, the voice he'd recognized since birth, a voice unaffected by her weakened condition of the last six months, Vida Mae spoke three words very clearly.

"Just love 'em."

Turning her face away, she laid her head down, resuming the labored, open-mouthed breathing.

Johnny sat in stunned silence, wide eyes blinking, heart waiting and hoping for another remarkable recovery, however brief, to hear Mother speak again. But it was not to be.

Those were the last words Johnny's sweet mother ever said.

He thought about those three little words all the way home and came to a conclusion. He heard the Good Lord give him one final, very poignant morsel of wisdom and life instruction through his mother. Johnny knew this affirmed Jesus' last words to his disciples about the two most important commandments from which all the law and other commandments rested. Namely, to love the Lord with all one's heart and soul and mind and love others as oneself.

This is the bare bones of Christianity. This was Mother's way. Just love 'em. Love 'em all.

Johnny remembered a Mother's Day card given to Susie when Travis and Faith were little kids. Travis wrote something very cute, but Faith, who was about five, took a long time to try putting her love for Mom into words. When she did, her dad thought it was the best description of pure love he'd ever read.

Faith wrote in a lopsided child's script, "I love you all that I can be." Susie cried.

Vida Mae Anderson goes home after giving 102 years of blessings to the world, but the blessings carry on.

Two days after Mother's sweet words, Johnny got a call to hurry back as the end was near. As he drove, fear came over him. It was as if the preparations for this moment flew out the window, and he was a scared little boy whose mother would be leaving forever. Johnny's speeding truck approached the exit for Crossroads Fellowship Houston, his beloved church. He'd called Pastor Mike Allard earlier to notify him he couldn't attend the board meeting scheduled that evening. Johnny felt a desperate need for prayer. He pulled off Beltway 8 and wheeled into the church parking lot.

Crossroad Fellowship's board consisted of ten guys whom he knew well and trusted completely. They gathered around Johnny, placing hands upon his shoulders, and prayed with compassionate hearts. Johnny felt the despairing spirit leave. Peace filled his soul.

Three hours later, on March 27, 2017, it happened. Vida Mae Anderson, the little girl whose faith inspired an evangelist to spark revival 98 years ago, who, in her lifetime, heard the voice of God himself, becoming one of His great intercessors, and who served up a refreshing smile to the world, went gently home to be with her Savior.

Her smile, however, remained in the hearts of her family along with all who'd ever known Vida Mae. It's still serving.

As he and Susie visited her grave later that year, Johnny noticed several wildflowers ruffling in the gentle breeze around Mother's tombstone. Most were buttercups, but one small batch of purple blooms stood out. He pictured Vida Mae smiling in Heaven as he plucked one of the little wild orchid blooms and tenderly laid it upon her headstone. The little flower looked happy there.

Johnny remembered her last instructions all year. He began to have urgings to go on one of the mission trips that Crossroads sponsored. The church is very mission-oriented, but Johnny never thought seriously about going. Too much activity in his life with a big family, ten acres to keep at home, and 90 acres in the country, all while working a full-time job as the Safety & HR Manager for Dynamic Products, Inc., a steel pipe fitting manufacturer.

But the urges wouldn't stop. They increased, and the focus was the annual mission trip to Kenya. Johnny finally admitted to himself the Good Lord was giving him a directive and asked for confirmation on the way to church. That Sunday, after praise and worship, Pastor Mike stepped forward and commented before beginning his message. He said, "You know, last year on our mission trip to Kenya..."

Johnny couldn't hear the rest due to the ringing in his ears at such a fast confirmation. Later, when he told the missions coordinator, Duane Cannon, and Pastor Mike he was signing up for Kenya, they were both elated. Then Johnny said, "But I don't know what use a guy my age will be to you on this trip."

Pastor Mike looked at him and said, "You can be like a grandpa to those little kids there. Many of them don't have parents or grandparents. You can give them what they yearn for most.

"You can just love 'em."

Johnny subdued his trepidations with prayer, received a volley of vaccinations required of international visas, and embarked a jetliner with the Crossroads mission team for a trip around the world, destination: Kenya. There, in the poverty-stricken backroads of Kajiado, he fell deeply in love with the local Maasai people. He was hooked. The following year, while in an isolated tiny tin shack set in the rolling countryside of Kenya, Johnny had the most powerful encounter with the awesome presence of God he'd ever experienced in his life.

There, on a trip wherein his intent was to give back the

many blessings bestowed upon him, Johnny's heart received from God the true immensity of the little phrase, "Just love 'em."

But then, that's another story for another time...

ABOUT THE AUTHOR

A native Texan, John Doyle Anderson was raised by hardy saints of the Greatest Generation who loved God and family, worked hard, and laughed often. He is a family man, Africa missions volunteer, and confessed late bloomer.

An inherited love of the outdoors is exceeded only by his God-given hankering to share encouraging truths of victory over life's adversities, resulting from relationships of faith in Christ. John and his wife Susie live near Crosby, Texas, and their six grown kids, along with nine grandkids, all live in the eastern portion of the state.

John's second book, Unstrangled, is coming soon in 2022.

Other Books by the Author

UNSTRANGLED

A story of men, abortion, regret, and redemption

Coming 2022…

Made in the USA
Middletown, DE
09 April 2022

63885745R00176